INVEST IN LIVING

GW00643892

HOME HONEY PRODUCTION

by

W. B. BIELBY

EP Publishing Limited
1977

The *Invest in Living* Series

About the Author

Bill Bielby has been Adviser in Beekeeping to North Yorkshire since 1974, before which he was Adviser to the West Riding County Council. An experienced lecturer, he spoke at the Helsinki Symposium of 1974 on the subject of 'The Wintering of Bees in Cold Climates'. He is a specialist in insulation and condensation problems in beehives and has introduced several innovations to beekeeping, including the disc entrance for beehives, the polypropylene brood frame and the catenary hive. His ambition is to increase home honey production and eventually export English honey. He discovered a colony of native British Bees at Fountains Abbey in 1966 and believes that this strain of bee could be the basis of increased production in northern latitudes not only in the UK but elsewhere in the Northern Hemisphere. He is primarily concerned with introducing bees to younger generations, especially in schools and colleges.

Copyright © EP Publishing Ltd 1977

ISBN 0 7158 0452 9

Published 1977 by EP Publishing Ltd, East Ardsley, Wakefield, West Yorkshire WF3 2JN

Printed and bound in Brighton, England by G Beard & Son Ltd

Contents

Bees

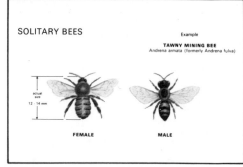

SOLITARY BEES

Example

TAWNY MINING BEE
Andrena armata (formerly Andrena fulva)

actual size
12 - 14 mm

FEMALE

MALE

Bees can be divided into three groups: solitary bees, social bees and advanced social bees. All are beneficial to mankind, and whilst the majority of people look upon the bee as a producer of honey and wax, the value of bees as pollinators of plants far exceeds their value as honey producers. So by becoming a honey producer, or even attempting to produce honey, you are indirectly helping to make a more fertile and prosperous world.

Solitary Bees

About 20 species exist in the British Isles. Have you observed the half-moon shaped cuttings out of rose leaves? The culprit is the leaf cutter bee, *Megachile.* The portions of leaf are used in the construction of the nest. Have you observed the small mounds of sandy soil raised on lawns and at the sides of sandy or fine gravel paths? The builder is a solitary bee, *Andrena armata.* The tunnel leads to cells excavated by the female. The female solitary bee manufactures a small pellet of pollen and honey on which an egg is laid—one in each cell. The egg becomes a larva which feeds on the honey/pollen pellet, and the following year adult solitary bees pop out of the tunnel to begin the life-cycle again. The most significant point in the behaviour of these solitary bees is that

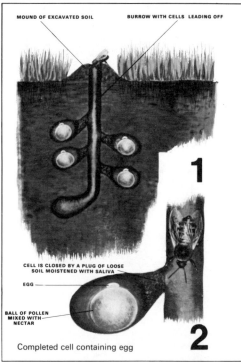

MOUND OF EXCAVATED SOIL

BURROW WITH CELLS LEADING OFF

1

CELL IS CLOSED BY A PLUG OF LOOSE SOIL MOISTENED WITH SALIVA

EGG

BALL OF POLLEN MIXED WITH NECTAR

Completed cell containing egg

2

(1). Most of the bees of the world are solitary, i.e. a single female is entirely responsible for making the nest and collecting the food needed for the development of her young; she usually dies before they emerge from their cells. *Andrena armata* prefers to nest in sandy soil under short grass, and is commonly found in lawns and golf courses
(2). The female lays a single egg in each cell, on a ball of food (pollen mixed with nectar) which will be sufficient for the complete development of the larva hatching from the egg. This method of food supply is called 'mass provisioning'

B

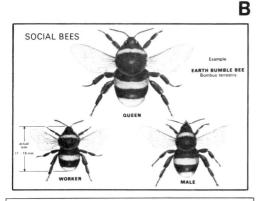

SOCIAL BEES

Example
EARTH BUMBLE BEE
Bombus terrestris

QUEEN

actual size
11 - 19 mm

WORKER

MALE

C

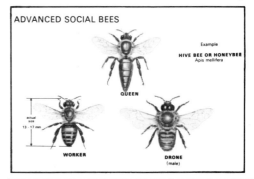

ADVANCED SOCIAL BEES

Example
HIVE BEE OR HONEYBEE
Apis mellifera

QUEEN

actual size
13 - 17 mm

WORKER

DRONE
(male)

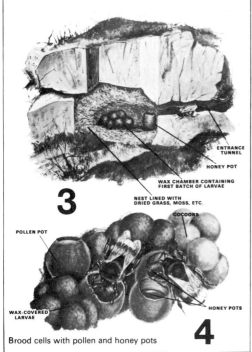

ENTRANCE TUNNEL

HONEY POT

WAX CHAMBER CONTAINING FIRST BATCH OF LARVAE

NEST LINED WITH DRIED GRASS, MOSS, ETC.

3

COCOONS

POLLEN POT

WAX-COVERED LARVAE

HONEY POTS

4

Brood cells with pollen and honey pots

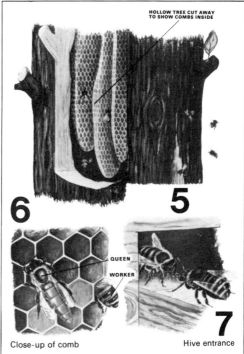

HOLLOW TREE CUT AWAY TO SHOW COMBS INSIDE

6

5

QUEEN

WORKER

Close-up of comb

7

Hive entrance

(3). Social bees live in family units (colonies). A single female (the queen) lays the eggs, and her older offspring (the workers) remain with her to forage and care for the later broods. *Bombus terrestris* builds her nest underground. The first batch of eggs is laid on a bed of pollen in a wax cell. The queen incubates them with the warmth of her body. The larvae from these eggs eat the pollen and also receive regurgitated food from the queen

(4). The later batches of brood are fed entirely on regurgitated food given to them at intervals by both queen and workers. This is called 'progressive feeding'

(5). Some social bees live in large and elaborately organised colonies. Surplus food is stored in combs and used in winter or times of scarcity. *Apis mellifera*, often called the hive bee, is equally at home in a hollow tree. Worker bees build the combs with wax secreted from their bodies; they do many different jobs, depending on their age and the needs of the colony

(6). Some cells of the comb serve as a nursery for the brood, the larvae being fed and kept warm by the workers. The workers also feed the queen and the drones (males)

(7). Food is often passed from one worker to another

the female does not incubate the eggs or feed the larvae. These bees are not known to overwinter as adult insects. There are males and females but no queen solitary bees.

Social Bees (Bumble Bees)

There are several species of bumbles in the British Isles, and most people are familiar with the large yellow-banded queens which appear in springtime in our gardens. Those with white tails are *Bombus lucorum.* Whilst bumblebees forage for pollen and honey, mankind does not use these bees for honey production. These fascinating bees live in a small colony during the summer months, but only the queens live through the winter, emerging in spring to replenish body fats before starting a nest and establishing a new colony in some hole in the ground or in decayed vegetation on the surface. The significant difference between bumblebees and solitary bees is that the queen (a fully developed female) does incubate her eggs and does feed her larvae. Also, only the queens overwinter; although in warm climates, small colonies may survive.

Advanced Social Bees (Honeybees)

Honeybees are warm temperate and sub-tropical animals.

For some 30 million years honeybees *(Apis mellifera)* have lived in the natural forests of the world, building their homes (nests) of wax honeycomb in hollow trees. The significant difference between honeybees and bumble bees is the fact that honeybees live as a colony throughout the year, and cannot exist as individuals for more than a few hours; whereas only the queen bumble bee survives the winter.

A colony of honeybees depends for survival on its ability to gather and store enough food to maintain life during the long periods when no food is available, i.e. no nectar (the carbohydrate) and no pollen (the protein).

For the greater part of the year, a honeybee colony consists of one queen (fully developed female), thousands of workers (females) and for a few months in summer, drones. The latter are the males of the species, which, poor things, are turned out to die towards the end of summer. For survival of the species, honeybees must produce more honey than they might need—enough in fact to enable at least some colonies to survive the successive years of bad summers which are an inevitable part of the weather cycle. This is the key to honey production. The beekeeper takes advantage of the honeybees' natural survival behaviour and removes the honey which is surplus to the requirements of the bees.

The bees gather *nectar* (a sugary solution) from plants which have *nectaries* (membraneous organs which produce nectar). As soon as the nectar passes into the bees' body, the nectar starts to become *honey*—a sweet liquid. Bees produce other substances such as *wax*, from which they construct their honeycomb, and *propolis* (before the city) which may be described as 'bee glue', a resinous material gathered mainly from trees and used to seal the joints and small fissures in the walls of the hive.

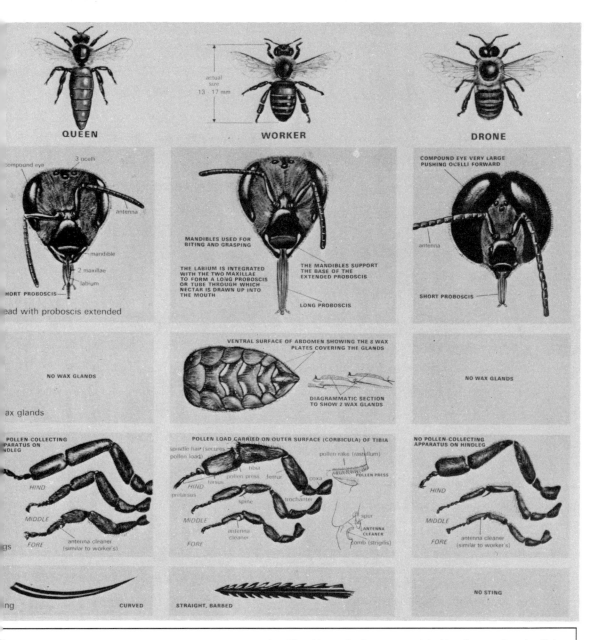

The queen and worker honeybees are female and the drone is male. There is normally only one queen in a colony, and she lays all the eggs. There are many workers (say 50,000 in summer), and they do almost all the work. In summer there may be a few hundred drones, but these die before winter.

What each worker bee does depends on her age and on the varying needs of the colony. Young bees work in the hive, first cleaning out used brood cells, and later feeding the brood, the queen and the drones. Some secrete wax for building or repairing the combs, process the nectar into honey, and pack pollen in the cells. Other bees guard the colony, using their stings if necessary.

The older worker bees go out of the hive, first on orientation flights and then to forage for what the colony requires: nectar, pollen, water or propolis (bee glue). Nectar is the carbohydrate food of bees, whereas pollen is a protein food, important for young workers, larvae, and the queen. Water may be needed by the bees feeding brood; also, in hot weather, bees collect and evaporate it to cool the hive. Water and nectar are carried in the honey sac, and so cannot be seen; pollen and propolis are brought home on the hindlegs. The legs, as well as the four wings, are attached to the thorax, which contains the muscles that enable the bee to walk and fly. The head contains several important glands, and the abdomen contains the honey sac as well as digestive and sting organs.

7

Scent Glands

Bees exposing scent glands (gland of Nasanov) while feeding at a dish of sugar syrup. These glands are near the tips of their bodies, and the smell from them attracts other bees to the food

Worker honeybees evicting drone

A beehive is a container for a honeybee's home and can be any one of hundreds of different shapes and sizes —not necessarily to suit the inmates, but to suit the beekeeper who generally has a mania for right angles, rectangles, sloping roofs and door steps!

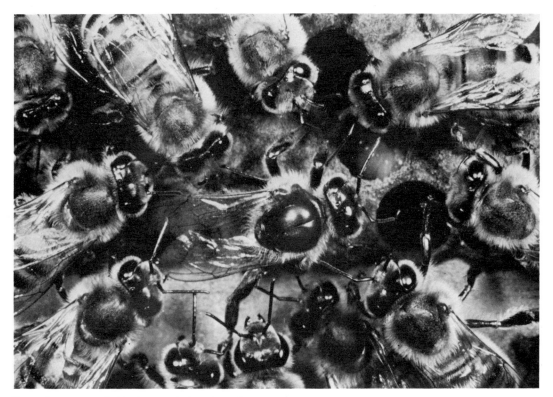

Queen bee surrounded by her court of workers; her
abdomen cannot be seen, because she is laying an
egg on the base of the cell

Basic Requirements for Honey Production

The basic requirements are:
- nectar, major sources of
- honeybees, colonies at strength
- weather, fine and warm.

Abundant Nectar

Bees cannot produce honey without an abundant supply of nectar. Surplus quantities of honey (i.e. honey stored beyond the requirements of the bees) are produced during relatively short periods when specific crops/plants are in flower. The whole complex processes can be reduced to a simple equation:

$H - h = S$ where H represents the total amount of honey produced by the bees; h represents the total amount of honey consumed by the bees, and the difference S represents the total amount of honey surplus to the requirements of the bees.

H – the total amount the bees may produce—can be *increased* by moving the bees to major sources of nectar (e.g. avenues of sycamores, hawthorn, rape, lime, clover, heather, etc.). Get to know your local sources of nectar.

h – the total amount the bees consume, may be *decreased* by reducing the rate of loss of heat from the colony by insulating hives and siting hives in sheltered positions. Minimum stress and interference by the apiarist are important factors in the 'well-being' of a colony of bees.

And so any steps the apiarist can take to increase H and decrease h will result in a larger S (surplus of honey). Even in beekeeping, one cannot escape from the simple maths and physics learned at school.

Honeybee Colonies at Strength

Without colonies at strength you cannot produce honey. The craft of beekeeping really amounts to the ability of the apiarist to maintain his many colonies of bees at peak strength for all the major honey flows in his locality throughout the season. Such colonies are called **Honey Production Colonies**.

The apiarist is a strategist. He unites his weaker colonies to produce an effective force of foraging bees in the right place at the right time. He is aware that colonies having young and vigorous queens are most profitable. It is unfortunate that bee behaviour can only be described in terms of human behaviour, so frail and ignorant is man. Nevertheless, the apiarist understands that bees do what they do in response to various stimuli, and furthermore they cannot help doing it! Bees respond (are sensitive!) to certain vibrations (frequencies) ranging from low audio up the audio range, as well as to electro magnetic/static radiations in the light frequency band up to ultra violet.[*] They are sensitive to small changes in temperature and their mode

* Refer to *Bees: Their Vision, Chemical Senses and Language* by Prof. Karl von Frisch.

of existence; indeed their very existence is only possible between certain limits of temperature.* Study the behaviour of the honeybee yourself and don't take too much notice of old bee-keepers. But listen and learn. You will find that bees produce other products in addition to honey, wax and propolis. Bees produce substances which influence the behaviour of the whole colony. These substances are called **pheromones**. They also produce venom which influences the behaviour of the beekeeper.

Fine Weather

The major source is about to flower. The colonies are at peak strength. They have room to store honey. *It all depends on the weather,* and local weather conditions vary enormously. In the UK, a good summer means a good surplus and a poor summer produces a poor harvest. But you will find that local weather conditions vary considerably and even in a generally poor summer, there are apiaries which produce a reasonable surplus. The gradients of the land, contours, power stations, etc. may cause local cloud formation, thus depleting the hours of sunshine over a considerable area. Cool air pours down hillsides into cosy valleys where permanent residence in a cold bath would be better than living in a beehive. You will find more about the weather and its subtle effects on behaviour in the chapter on swarming (pages 21–8).

The basic requirements will always be major sources of nectar, honeybee colonies at strength and fine weather all at the same time! So it becomes a gamble; but you are a sporting man, so read on.

* Refer to *The Behaviour and Social Life of Honeybees* by Ronald Ribbands (B.R.A.).

Clothing and Equipment

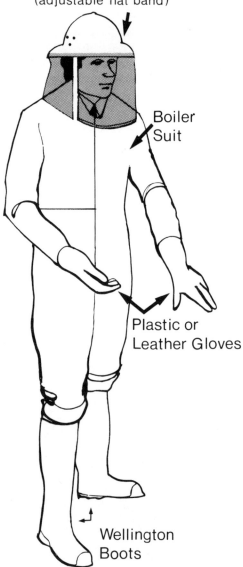

Helmet & Ring Veil
(adjustable hat band)

Boiler Suit

Plastic or Leather Gloves

Wellington Boots

Keeping bees to produce honey is not easy and can be dangerous.

Protective Clothing

Times have changed during the last 50 years. We are largely a consumer society and folks starting to keep bees now look to some appliance dealer for purchasing the necessities.

Veil: now when I was a lad, we had to ask mother if she had any old net curtains she did not use and make a veil to protect the head and neck from stings. We cut a 6 in. square and stitched some darker net to the lighter material which reflected the light and was not easy to see through. Cost was nil. If you buy a veil it will cost at least £2.40 inc. VAT (1976 prices). Now if you are wealthy enough that is fine, but the only vat you should enthuse about is a vat full of honey!

Boiler suit (beeproof): with zip and buttons. Sew up the slots for gaining access to your trouser pockets or the bees will . . . A boiler suit is a good investment because it can be used for many other jobs in addition to protecting you from angry bees. Cost—at least £2.40 (1976 prices).

Gloves: special gauntlet gloves are obtainable. Plastic gloves are cheaper than leather and more durable but perhaps a little clumsy. Cost—£1.40 to £3.50 (1976). Some beginners are successfully managing with the rubber washing-up gloves available at chemists' shops. Others are not. You must be able to work without being stung.

Boots: Wellington boots are essential for battling beekeepers; especially if the bees are noted for their prowess at ankle tapping. As bees tend to walk in an upward direction, tuck your trouser legs well inside the boots for safety.

Equipment

Smoker: a device with bellows in which some material (touch-wood is pretty good) is burnt to produce smoke which tends to subdue bees. The theory is that they smell the smoke and think the forest is on fire. In preparation to abandon their home, they gorge themselves on honey and in so doing are less likely to sting the beekeeper. Some keepers use corrugated cardboard because it is convenient, but sometimes the stuff is flameproof and goes out. Choose a material which gives off a pleasant smoke (peat is good)—you might as well enjoy the smell instead of nearly suffocating. And for heaven's sake, don't pump smoke into a beehive—just think of each bee with its 5,000 little eyes watering as a result of those tiny droplets of tarry oil being blown in. Little more than the sight of smoke on the horizon is necessary! Cost—anything up to £15.00 for a clockwork smoker! But you could make one if you are a keen DIY man. Cheapest is about £2.50 (1976).

Hive tool: a specially designed instrument for prizing top bars of honeycombs loose and for scraping and general use whilst manipulating hives. Regularly lost in the grass if not painted yellow. A paint scraper will suffice.

Cloths: three cloths 508 mm × 406 mm (20 in. × 16 in.) or 457 mm × 457 mm (18 in. × 18 in.) are needed for covering the bees during manipulation. These cloths should be of a flannelette type material (an old flannel bed sheet cut to size would be suitable). Soak in water and gently squeeze so that water is not actually dripping from them. They can be used to cover the tops of combs not actually being examined. To repel bees sprinkle the equivalent of a teaspoonful of Benzaldehyde evenly over the cloths. Over-use of Benzaldehyde will drive the bees out of the hive!

Hives: the one factor completely within the control of the honey producer is the type and design of the hive he wishes to house his bees in. For honey production, hives must be easily closed and made safe for transportation. For the businessman, capital invested for a good return is sound economics and the DIY man can make £100 produce 30 hives and a tonne of honey in two reasonably good years. But see the chapter on 'Hives' (pages 29–32).

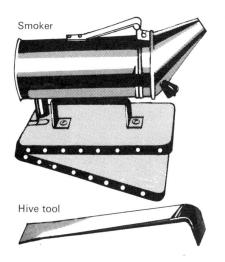

Smoker

Hive tool

Before Buying your Bees

Before buying your bees read books, e.g. *A Complete Guide to Beekeeping,* by Roger A. Morse (Pelham). This book makes excellent reading for the beginner and gives almost complete guidance at your stage of progress. Many books confuse by offering systems of management and methods of beekeeping without teaching the student beekeeper to understand the insect and its behaviour. In the past this may have led to countless disasters.

Associations

Just because Foulshams forecast a good summer don't rush off and buy your bees. You want to know what you are doing in more ways than one. Join the local Beekeepers' Association. Attend their meetings and demonstrations. In some districts, there are courses organised by the Education authorities. You will make friends in beekeeping circles. As a beekeeper, you will find that wherever you go in this world, no matter to which country or continent, the common factor of beekeeping will ensure you a welcome and hospitality. The Bee Research Association,* an international organisation, has a 'Meet the Beekeeper Scheme' and lists names and addresses of beekeepers world-wide who offer their hospitality to visiting keepers from other countries.

The First Steps

First you must decide how many bees you will need to get your beekeeping under way. Do you want to start off with a stock of bees, a colony of bees or a nucleus?

These terms are defined by the British Standard Specification 1372/1957.

- **Stock:** includes Bees and Hive
- **Colony:** bees on not less than six British Standard Brood combs (number of combs must be specified); not less than four combs if Langstroth or Modified Dadant ('Types of Hive', see pages 29–32).
- **Nucleus:** British Standard Brood frames, not more than five combs; Langstroth or MD not more than three combs.
- the **Queen** must be a this year's queen or her age must be specified. (Take a tip and insist on a young queen—this year reared.)

*International Bee Research Association, Hill House, Chalfont St. Peter, Gerrards Cross, Bucks.

How Much Will it Cost?

How deep is your pocket? Let us assume you wish to start off with one colony in one hive. You will need a second hive if you have a swarm. One begets two; two may become three or four stocks, and so on.

Beginners' Outfits

The cost of hives and equipment is oppressive to the craft. The appliance dealers are offering Beginners' Outfits (1976) for £74.00. These include your colony of bees, queen excluder, two supers (for honey storage) with frames and foundation, crown board, roof, veil, gloves and smoker. This is cheaper than buying separate items. So at this rate, at those prices, without inflation, you will have spent about £600 before you exceed the 10-hive barrier and transcend from Hobbyist to Sideliner.

Unless you stumble across a bargain, e.g. some poor widow selling her deceased's apiary before becoming acquainted with the real value of bees and equipment, you are going to have to fork out. Beware of bee pedlars; snapping up bees in one part of Britain and selling in another is one way of spreading the Foul Brood diseases about which you will have to know.

However, do not be daunted. This is the age of DIY and if you are handy with a hammer you too can bash a hive together. Using material to hand and working to strict dimensions, you can reduce expenditure to a minimum. It would be fair to warn you that your first two pounds of honey could cost you £40 per pound! Conversely, you may produce enough honey in your first year completely to cover your capital outlay. Either way, or mid-way, it is certain that you will perspire and lose pints under the veil, almost certainly you will shed blood, at worst you could be pricked on the backside by a thistle, stung on the hand by a nettle and get one on the nose from a bee within a matter of seconds. And it hurts. (See 'Stings', page 59.)

You now have an idea of the costs of Home Honey Production. When you give away that jar of beautiful honey or a delicately moulded beeswax candle as a present for Christmas, only you will know the cost and suffering, the agonies of beekeeping. But it is all surpassed by the sheer joy of the challenge, the pleasure of the sounds of bees, the scent of wax, honey and propolis, and the glorious end products: honey for sweetness, wax for warmth and light, and propolis for healing.

Where Should you Live?

The Best Areas

Up to the 1950s, the country bee-keeper produced most honey, especially if he lived on land with a magnesium limestone subsoil. All plants secrete more nectar when grown in such districts. A study of the geology of the UK will show the limestone belts running down the north-east counties and crossing the centre of England through the Chiltern and Cotswold hills.

The finest clover honey has been produced on the Yorkshire Wolds. Clover is good for sheep and adds nitrogen to the soil. Modern methods of intensive agriculture have reduced the acreage of clover which has historically provided the major honey flow in June and July. Very many other factors influence nectar secretion, e.g. weather, temperature, etc., and the beginner is advised to read the Bee Research Association book *Honey*, Section 1.

Urban Bees

Intensive agriculture has put an end to the days when beekeeping was a rural pursuit. The urban beekeeper has recently become the more successful honey producer. Gardens and trees are important. Acer species can provide a major honey flow in the spring. Sycamore trees may blossom over a period of four or five weeks. Disused railway tracks and embankments, desolate areas, parks and gardens will often produce a wealth of nectar sources, but beware of valley bottoms and frost pockets.

However, do not expect to put a couple of hives down at the bottom of the garden and become a producer of honey. If this does happen, you are lucky to be living in an unusually good district. If after two or three years, you have had lots of swarms (see 'Swarming', pages 21–8) and no surplus honey, it is more than likely you are living in a poor district. Contrary to most opinions and traditional writing about the subject of swarming, it is a scientific fact that a dearth of nectar is more likely to cause a colony to swarm than a heavy flow of nectar.

Out-Apiaries

If you live at the bottom of a wooded valley containing lots of flowering trees such as wild cherry, chestnut, sycamore, lime, etc., it would be very tempting to say 'Yes, you should do well here.' But the only way to find out is to keep bees! Much better if you are living a few hundred feet above on a hillside. Anyway, 'Home Honey Production' does not really mean that you necessarily have to keep your livestock within eyesight. The bee-keepers' jargon includes the expression 'out-apiary' which is an apiary in some favoured spot at a distance from your home. Your beekeeping will be better and your production higher when you use an out-apiary, because you will have to think more about what you are going to do whenever you visit it. You will only interfere with the bees after careful preparation. Remember that the bees maintain temperature and humidity within fine limits, and when you open up a hive, the bees have work to do.

Sites for Apiaries

Consideration for Others

In choosing a place for your bees, you must give the utmost consideration to other people, some of whom may not share your fanatical enthusiasm or relish the idea of an occasional bolt into the coal house to escape the attentions of angry bees. You may think it funny when your previously friendly neighbour (whose cat regularly scratches up your newly sown seeds) confronts you with one eye completely closed and the other eye half-open peering angrily over a fiery red nose, his wife already having mentioned that your bees ruined her whiter than white washing early in the spring. Well, it's *not funny.* You must be prepared to move your bees to another site if they interfere with any other person's lawful pursuits.

Many beekeepers have successfully produced honey without causing any trouble whatsoever, from hives kept in their gardens with good neighbours on both sides. Generally they have created an enclosure, a high hedge or tall shrubs or small trees, to force the bees to a higher altitude so that the flight path is well above nuisance height. Some people go berserk if they even see a hive, regardless of whether it is empty or seething with bees; so, point No. 1, keep the hives out of sight. Another good reason for keeping hives out of view is the temptation which they offer to intrepid youths with nothing better to do than issue a challenge to their mates to 'push it over' and retreat and watch the fun from a safe distance. Vandalism is to be reckoned with these days and should be a factor to be considered when choosing an out-apiary site. Theft is also a possibility, and it is sad to say that beekeepers in other countries do not seem to have these problems to the same extent. Bee rustling is an offence, for which one can think of much more appropriate punishments than a fine.

Direction of Comb Building

Because it has been shown that bees build honeycomb* under some influence of the earth's magnetic field, hives should be positioned so that comb building will be along magnetic north to south. There should be room to operate comfortably from the rear. Remember the old saying, 'the front of a horse, the back of a hive of bees'; and by the way, bees don't like horses nor do they like sweaty feet, so wear wellington boots to protect the ankles. Nor does their temper improve if the operator reeks of onions or beer. It is not known how they react to the smell of mead in one's breath.

It is thought in some quarters that if the hive entrances face east or south-east, the early morning sun will make the bees start work earlier than they would do otherwise. Hives should be level—use a spirit level—as combs are also built under the influence of gravity.

Finally, in choosing the site for an apiary, remember that bees cannot beget honey if there is no honey to be got and success depends on ample sources of nectar being available within a short distance of the colonies.

* Refer to *Bee World*, Vol. 55, No. 4, 1974, 'Directions in which Bees Build Combs', Eva Crane.

Colonies at Strength

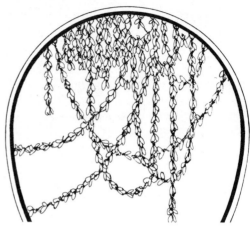

When wax is being made, bees hang in festoons and remain motionless for about 24 hours whilst little wax scales exude from four pairs of glands under their abdomens. The scales are moved to the mouth parts and forelegs and used for comb building. A true DIYS operation—they produce all their own material and carry out the work

What is a 'strong colony' of bees? How many bees are there in a strong colony? Do we mean strong in numbers or strong in vigour? The meteorological boys use the Beaufort Scale to describe the strength of the wind, but unfortunately we do not have a force 8 colony of bees. Furthermore, some colonies of bees become abnormally strong in numbers of bees for several reasons. Do we want abnormally strong (vast numbers) of bees in our hives? It does not follow that the strongest in numbers get the most honey. Just look at the human race. Take India and her teeming millions—not much surplus food there! The way to get honey is to have as many stable colonies of bees in many apiaries (bee yards) of about 20 stocks each in good honey-producing districts. More than 20 hives in one place may saturate an area— i.e., too many bees for too few flowers.

Management of Colonies

The growth and decline in the population of a colony of bees is a function of the availability of food, which in turn is directly a function of the seasons, flora, temperatures and other factors.

When the flowers are out in spring and the weather is fine and warm, you feel good, the bees feel good. They wax strong and multiply. Incoming nectar and fresh pollen—carbohydrate and protein—builds bonny babies. The worker bees involuntarily secrete wax which is used to build honeycomb to store honey. You must see to it that they have just enough room to do what they want to do. They want to build comb and store honey, so *you* give them the facility required by placing wax foundation (sheet of wax with honeycomb imprint to assist the bees to build comb where required) in the best place in the hive for the bees to build comb. They also need to build new comb for brood rearing. The number of sheets of foundation you give and the frequency you give it should depend entirely on the needs of the colony—e.g., in early spring you need give very little, perhaps only one sheet of foundation. Several days later, when the colony is stronger, you

should give perhaps two or three foundations placed over and to the side of the centre of the expanding nest.

If you have the national type hive (with British Standard Frames), *do not* be tempted into using a second brood box because the single brood box appears to be (and is often) too small.

Restriction of the laying room of queens does not precipitate the building of queen cells and swarming. You are aiming to produce honey, and you will get more pots of honey if you use a single brood chamber; and your relations with the bees will be happier. The regular withdrawal of the oldest brood comb (be it full of brood, honey, etc., or not) and its replacement with a frame of foundation on the flanks of the brood is good management if carried out during a honey flow. ('What shall I do with the old comb?' Answer: 'burn it.') The well-being of the bees is paramount, and as long as they are expanding (or think they are expanding —fooled by your wizardry) and building comb they are stable and not going to swarm. So this is a good situation.

Supering

Supering means adding room for honey storage. A colony of bees at strength during a major honey flow can fill a honey super in seven days. Supering is an art, and will be a very satisfying expertise for you to develop. First it is important to appreciate exactly when a colony is ready to accept its first super. It is not merely a matter of putting on a super because there is a honey flow. The make-up of the super is important, and the timing of the operation (it should not take more than a few seconds actually to do the job) ought to be thought of as critical! The odds are that you will not be at home at 20 minutes past 11 on the day that first super should be added—but if it happens to be a weekend it should be possible! So you have to become very much aware of conditions within the hive in spring when the honey starts to pour in. Ideally, it should be just when the last few pounds of last year's winter stores have been consumed—a knife-edge situation because a bad turn in the weather could result in the starvation and death of the colony. A perfect situation would be for nearly all the winter stores to have been turned into brood and bees! You do not want incoming honey to occupy good breeding space in the brood nest, so look out for honey being stored in the top corners of the brood combs and put on the first super *before* that honey is capped; but only if the good weather is forecast to continue! To give a super in the face of bad weather is harmful to the colony. If the bees cannot use it immediately it may become alien to them, and they may not go into it later when the weather improves.

The first super can be made up from drawn comb with perhaps one or two sheets of wax foundation placed towards the outside of the super, preferably between very straight drawn combs.

The second super should be given if the weather and honey flow prospects are good and when the outside combs are half-filled with honey (not half-capped!). The two outside combs in this half-filled condition should be transferred into the centre of the new super. Fully sealed combs (or nearly so) should be moved to the flanks of the first super and a couple of foundations placed in the centre. Thus you have started off the filling of the second box by giving the two combs with bees and honey. This second box should contain at least 50 per cent wax foundation. Subsequent supers should have more foundation included.

Always put new supers on top. You can go on adding supers until a ladder is needed to look in the top and you will need a wheelbarrow to carry away the harvest.

Swarming

The best way to start beekeeping is to acquire a prime swarm; especially if it is free. The wise men of apiculture will shake their heads miserably and say 'What about the possibility of disease?' Well you might get knocked down if you cross the road. Those same wise men will readily make the utmost use of a swarm themselves (they are jealous of your good fortune) because it is worth a silver spoon in June and a load of hay in May.

Swarming is the natural way for colonies of bees to multiply, and it behoves every apiarist to welcome it and exploit a natural phenomenon in the interests of honey production.

Study the bee and help her to do her thing. Bees do not live in a square world

A swarm is attracted to the bee bob by the scent left by previous swarms of bees. Attach a small canker of a tree to the under side of a crown board. This looks like a swarm from a distance. Burn some old wax on the bob to attract the swarm. The hole in the board can be made to close or open, thus permitting the bees to go through on to a box of foundation above

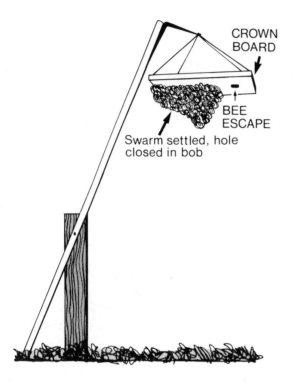

CROWN BOARD

BEE ESCAPE

Swarm settled, hole closed in bob

Baited Hives

Eight to twelve days before the swarm issues, bees are getting heavier with honey in their honey sacs (a worker bee has a honey sac or stomach and a true stomach between which there is a valve) in preparation for the great exodus. Some four or five days at least before swarming, a growing number of scout bees will be searching for a new home—an empty hive in a suitable situation or someone else's false roof, a hollow tree or a cavity in a wall. An empty hive with a very small entrance strategically placed will be very attractive to the scouts.* This hive is called a *'baited hive'* and will provide the ideal home for a swarm. In the first instance, the 'bait' is the odour of bees called 'footprint odour' which is attractive and common to all colonies of honeybees. This footprint odour is distinct from 'colony odour' which is colony specific and helps homing bees to be identified by their own guard bees before gaining admission to a hive. If the 'baited hive' happens to be a new hive and has not been inhabited by bees previously, then one well-used empty brood comb from an old hive will provide the necessary footprint odour. Another method of making a new hive attractive to a swarm is to burn some old beeswax inside the hive before setting the hive in a shady, peaceful corner of the garden. The baited hive should have enough room inside to allow the swarm (when it arrives) to do exactly what it wants to do: cluster and start building honeycomb. Do not fill the brood box with frames of foundation, just one old comb, say three or four sheets of foundation and then fill up the box 48 hours after the swarm has arrived, for by that time the new home will have been located and the bees will not abscond.

If the weather is fine, and there is a major source of nectar, the new brood box could be completed within a week and you will be able to put on a queen excluder (to confine the queen to the brood box) and a super for the bees to store honey for you. If the weather is bad, you must feed sugar syrup to

* Baited hives are regarded as 'foul play' and are illegal in some countries as they are a means of attracting other people's swarms! But not in the U.K.

prevent the swarm from starving to death. If the weather is changeable, sugar syrup will enable the swarm to get on with comb building and be in a position to get honey should the weather improve.

There are no rules in beekeeping. When the apiarist provides his bees with wax foundation (sheets of wax embossed with cell pattern), he is helping his bees to build comb in such a manner that he can lift out the comb for examination and various purposes. He should make it a rule that bees should *never* be given foundation which cannot be used immediately for comb building; i.e., never give foundation unless there is a honey flow taking place.* Bees secrete wax (from four pairs of wax glands) involuntarily during a honey flow. If fed sugar syrup, especially during the summer months, they will produce wax and continue comb building. Bees engaged in comb building are not going to swarm. A strong colony *not* building honeycomb when there is a honey flow on is almost certainly going to swarm.

Why Do Colonies Swarm?

The answer to this question is far from simple. Mention has already been made of young queens in this respect. Let us look more deeply into this intriguing activity. The queen honey-bee produces a complex substance we call 'Queen substance'. (This was recently discovered by Dr Colin Butler at Rothamsted Experimental Station, Harpenden, Herts., England.) As long as all the worker bees in the colony are aware (perhaps getting the scent) of an ample supply of this substance, they are inhibited from building queen cells, an activity which precedes swarming. Although there may be other causes, two causes are:

■ failure of the queen to produce enough queen substance
■ failure of the conditions within the hive to allow all the bees to be satisfied, even if the queen is producing an adequate supply of queen substance.

Queen Substance

Let us look into the causes of failure of the queen to produce enough queen substance:

■ **Age.** Whilst queens have been known to live for several years, it is an indisputable fact that colonies of bees having young queens are less likely to swarm than colonies with old queens; therefore it is sound policy to work as many colonies as possible with young queens for good honey production
■ **Weather.** A break in the weather during a honey flow will cause the bees to give less food to the queen. The immediate effect will be a reduction in the rate of egg laying *and* the amount of queen substance, producing an unfavourable situation in the colony. A large number of workers will not be getting their share of queen substance and will no longer be inhibited from building queen cells; thus a break in the weather can precipitate swarming
■ **Poor Queens.** Queens raised under adversity, in emergency or non-prosperous conditions are less able to satisfy a colony with queen substance than the large voluptuous ladies raised naturally under prosperous conditions.

---

*When you see bees shooting out of the hive like bullets from a gun—there is a honey flow on.

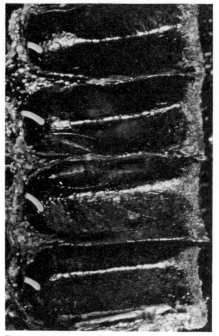
Eggs at bottom of cells

Honeybee pupae

Various stages of brood development

Many new beekeepers with one colony are prone to divide that colony in order to get a second colony. They have been told that the half without a queen will raise a new queen providing there are eggs in the combs. Absolutely true. But that new queen will be an 'emergency queen'—good enough to ensure the continuity of the species but very likely to fail soon and precipitate a swarm.

Never, never split a colony of bees like this. Just be patient and wait until the colony is producing queen cells

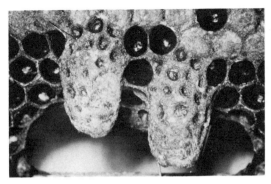

Queen cells

Queen cell opened to show mature larva

under prosperous conditions when it is about to divide naturally. The queens thus produced will be heavier and more reliable. This is the time for division.

Failure of Hive Conditions

Let us look into the causes of failure of conditions in the hive which may precipitate swarming:

- **Congestion.** This is generally the fault of the apiarist in not giving enough room for the bees to expand and store honey. A well-balanced colony can make rapid progress when confined to a compact hive space. Excellent—but rapid build up of bees results in traffic congestion, and the free exchange of queen substance throughout the bee colony is then restricted. Thus there can be a situation where there is a perfectly good queen and an excellent colony of bees forced into swarming by congestion. The smart apiarist is quick to recognise the need for more space to store honey and gives more room just when it is needed—he understands his bees and his sources of honey

- **Congestion.** From time to time, a colony of bees will build an arch of honey in the brood compartment, especially if the apiarist has been a little dilatory in supplying the first super. A state of congestion may occur if the bees continue to store in the brood compartment and ignore the new space provided.

To summarise the congestion syndrome: congestion prevents the free flow or free exchange of queen substance and bees are no longer inhibited from swarming. Good management can largely prevent this situation from developing.

Getting a Swarm

You should always have spare hives and equipment to deal successfully with a swarm. After all, we are talking about honey production, and a large swarm of bees has enormous potential for delivering the goods, if suitably exploited. The majority of apiarists in the UK regard swarming as something to be 'controlled' or 'prevented', and the main reason for this wretched attitude is the fear of losing a swarm that might issue whilst they are out at

work. So do not be bullied by the old hands into carrying out time-consuming manipulations and methods such as cutting out queen cells and hunting for queens. There are better ways of spending a Saturday afternoon.

Let us take the most likely situation with which you as a red raw beginner might find yourself having to cope. Somebody will let you know (with much excitement and a trace of a smirk on his face) that your bees are swarming or have just settled in the hedge at the bottom of next door's garden. You must somehow keep complete control of yourself. Thank the bringer of the good news and inform him that you were expecting this swarm and that you will deal with it

when you have had your coffee (would he mind if you came into his garden just to collect it, etc.). The bees will cluster for a while, and it is a good thing to give the swarm time to settle properly before collecting it. But don't wait too long—the scouts may already have a new abode earmarked. If the new abode is your very own baited hive—what could be better? If you have observed scouts investigating your hive in increasing numbers for the last few days then it is an almost sure thing (nothing in beekeeping is absolutely sure). But if you have not observed scouts then you must collect your first swarm and house it in such a manner that it will serve you best.

Skeps

A most useful piece of equipment for collecting a swarm is a skep. It is sometimes possible to use a plastic bag if the swarm is hanging in a pear-shaped cluster from a thin branch. Simply lift the bag up around the swarm and snip off offending twigs and branches until you can gently close and secure the bag with the swarm inside. Very impressive, the sheer simplicity and security of the operation (if you can see at the onset that this plastic bag method will work, there will be no harm in allowing an admiring group of spectators to form) will make you full of confidence. Next time you will do it without veil or gloves!

But swarms can be damnably awkward from time to time; that is, awkward to collect. That swarm in the hedge will need a skep or a wooden box or a brood box with a few combs and top cover placed in such a position that the bees will move upwards into the shade and protection of the box. You may have to wait until nightfall before the bees have finally moved up (bees move upwards much more readily than they will move downwards except when it is your neck or trousers). Sometimes you can shake the branch and dislodge the swarm so that the whole cluster will fall directly into the skep. Just before actually shaking the swarm off the branch, it is a good idea to place a nice white cloth on top of a crown board on the ground below. Having collected the swarm in the skep, gently lower it to the ground and invert it. Stand it on the cloth, placing a stick or a stone under one side to allow any flying bees

Skeps. George Hawthorne, Adviser in Beekeeping for Berkshire and Oxon, is the craftsman. Bees have been kept in skeps for over a thousand years

The straw was a cheap and plentiful material and gave the bees insulation from the cold of winter and the heat of summer

to join up. And if you have got the queen, they certainly will soon join the swarm.

The perfect swarm for collecting. A plastic bag can be gently placed round the swarm and held tightly at the neck whilst the branch is severed. The swarm can be hived or placed in a travelling box. The bees should not be exposed to the sun or kept for long in a closed plastic bag

You have Collected the Swarm

If it is from your own hive, then you must think carefully and change your attitude towards that hive. It is no longer a production unit. It contains few bees, queen cells and food. A fortnight ago it was storing honey at a fair old rate and everything to do with beekeeping was super. But now it has swarmed and you have collected the swarm. Excellent. Lift that hive off its site—to the left or to the right—about 600 mm (2 ft.). On the site place a floor-

board and one *shallow* box of drawn comb or foundation. On top of this box place a queen excluder. Next, one or two supers preferably with foundation. On top of all place the honey supers from the parent colony—honey and bees.

Hive the Swarm

Use a large board as a giant doorstep or gangway, and with a firm and well directed movement shake the bees on to the gangway leading to the new hive entrance. You will then see a glorious movement of bees (within a few seconds) up the incline towards and into the entrance of the new home. It is hard to resist trying to spot the queen as she moves with great dignity and haste over the shoulders of the workers apparently eager to get the new home established. But the energy of this swarm will not be dissipated in establishing a new brood nest because of the shallow box you have provided. The energy will largely go into the space above the queen excluder where the honey will be stored. Thus you will produce your honey and at least double the number of hives you started with. That parent colony (your attitude to which has changed!) could be divided into two parts, each with queen cells. You could successfully build up the two units for honey production next year, providing that the swarm and division have taken place early enough in the season, say the beginning of June or thereabouts—and of course, given good weather.

Making your Own Hives

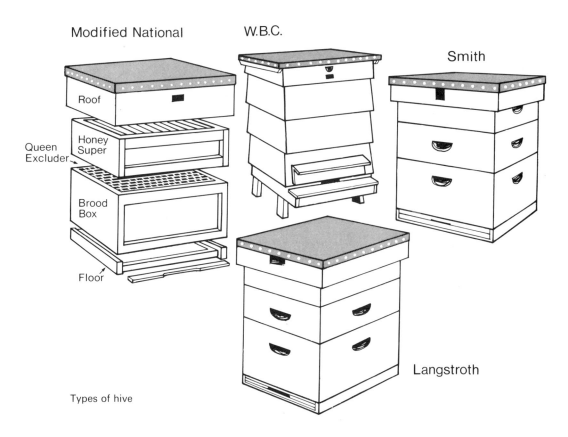

Modified National   W.B.C.   Smith

Roof

Queen Excluder

Honey Super

Brood Box

Floor

Langstroth

Types of hive

Clearly it is cheaper to be independent of suppliers of equipment, although beekeeping is undoubtedly served very well by appliance dealers all over the world.

Types of Hive

Langstroth: 95 per cent (approx.) of the world's apiaries are using the Langstroth Hive (Standard box 505 mm × 405 mm × 240 mm (19.8 in. × 15.9 in. × 9.4 in.). The external and internal measurements vary slightly but with some importance from country to country and within those countries.
W.B.C.: 53 per cent (approx.) of apiarists in the UK use the W.B.C. (William Broughton Carr) Hive. No details are given because this hive is not easily transportable to sources of nectar. The hive is not considered economical to construct or profitable in practice, except in static situations where migratory beekeeping is not necessary.
Modified National: over 40 per cent of apiarists in the UK use the Modified National Hive.

Table of Hive Dimensions for Home Constructors

	Langstroth Hive (New Zealand)	Modified National Hive *Metric measurements for standard equipment (see British Standard 1300:1960)*	Smith Hive *Metric measurements for standard equipment*
Standard brood box (full-depth Langstroth storey)			
Outer measurements:	505 mm × 405 mm × 240 mm	458 mm × 458 mm × 225 mm	463 mm × 416 mm × 225 mm
Inner measurements:	465 mm × 365 mm × 240 mm	425 mm × 365 mm × 225 mm	419 mm × 371 mm × 225 mm
Honey super (three-quarter depth Langstroth storey)			
Outer measurements:	505 mm × 405 mm × 185 mm	458 mm × 458 mm × 149 mm	463 mm × 416 mm × 149 mm
Inner measurements:	465 mm × 365 mm × 185 mm	425 mm × 365 mm × 149 mm	419 mm × 371 mm × 149 mm
Section super (half-depth Langstroth storey)			*Section rack* (for section carriers)
Outer measurements:	505 mm × 405 mm × 135 mm	458 mm × 458 mm × 114 mm	463 mm × 416 mm × 124 mm
Inner measurements:	465 mm × 365 mm × 135 mm	432 mm × 432 mm × 114 mm	419 mm × 371 mm × 124 mm
			See Ministry of Agriculture Fisheries & Food Advisory Leaflet 445
Rebate (for all three hive bodies)			
Depth without metal rabbet:	14 mm	14 mm	14 mm
Depth with metal rabbet:	20 mm	20 mm	20 mm
Rebate ledge:	10 mm	10 mm	10 mm
Brood and honey frames			
Top bar:	482 mm × 25 mm × 20 mm	432 mm × 22 mm × 17 mm	394 mm × 22 mm × 17 mm
Bottom bar:	450 mm × 25 mm × 10 mm	355 mm × 16 mm × 9 mm	355 mm × 16 mm × 9 mm
Depth of frame (End-bar length):	230 mm for standard box / 175 mm for honey super / 125 for section super	216 mm / 140 mm	216 mm / 140 mm
Frame spacing:	34 mm for brood frames / 43 mm for honey frames	38 mm	38 mm
(End-bar width):		38 mm	38 mm
Thickness of end-bar:	10 mm	10 mm	10 mm

Section frame (half- and full-depth)

Top bar:	482 mm × 38 mm × 8 mm	431 mm × 48 mm × 13 mm	394 mm × 48 mm × 13 mm
Bottom bar:	450 mm × 38 mm × 8 mm	354 mm × 48 mm × 13 mm	354 mm × 48 mm × 13 mm
Half-depth end bar:	126 mm × 45 mm × 8 mm	140 mm × 48 mm × 13 mm	140 mm × 48 mm × 13 mm
Full-depth end bar:	234 mm × 45 mm × 8 mm		

Section

Overall length:	428 mm	108 mm	108 mm
Sector lengths:	108 mm and 106 mm	108 mm	108 mm
Width:	45 mm	50 mm	50 mm
Thickness:	3 mm	Cut by special machinery to 3 mm	3 mm

Timber for sections
Bass or lime

Bottom board (reversible, non-reversible general specification)

Length:	505 mm minimum	458 mm	463 mm
Width:	405 mm	458 mm	416 mm
Side rim length:	505 mm	458 mm	463 mm
End rim length:	405 mm	458 mm	416 mm
Rim width:	20 mm	25 mm	25 mm
Entrance depth:	10 mm to 20 mm	10 mm to 20 mm	20 mm to 20 mm

Hive lid (standard telescopic)

Outer measurements:	505 mm × 450 mm × 95 mm	500 mm × 500 mm	494 mm × 437 mm
Inner measurements:	510 mm × 410 mm × 75 mm	475 mm × 475 mm	481 mm × 424 mm
Timber thickness:	20 mm	13 mm	No less than 13 mm
Insulation thickness:	Nil (optional)	50 mm	50 mm

Excluder rim, division board, inner cover

Outer rim measurements:	505 mm × 405 mm	458 mm × 458 mm	463 mm × 416 mm
Inner rim measurements:	465 mm × 365 mm	408 mm × 408 mm	438 mm × 391 mm
Lower rim depth:	6 mm (to ensure bee-space)	6 mm	6 mm
Upper rim depth:	4 mm (to ensure bee-space)	4 mm	4 mm

All measurements are subject to local variations and are for guidance only.

The question of top or bottom bee space is always under discussion, and the beginner is advised that he must be on guard against using equipment which does not ensure that a single bee space only (6.4 mm) occurs between top bars and comb/bottom bars of boxes, e.g. the use of framed queen excluders wire or zinc, can increase the space and cause excessive brace comb to be built.

British Deep: more efficient than the National and slightly cheaper for the following reasons. Only a single brood box is required; a larger area of comb is available for the queen, and there is ample room for winter stores. This reduces the number of frames required and reduces operating time.

Smith: mostly used in Scotland. Somewhat cheaper and easier to construct than the Modified National Hive.

Catenary Hive (Frameless): the prototypes of this hive have been used for ten years with varying degrees of success. In its original form, the hive was double walled and highly insulated. The name is derived from the Latin 'catena'—a chain. When a chain is suspended freely between two points, its shape is known as a catenary curve, and this is the natural shape of a honeycomb when bees build comb in a non-restricted space. Thus it is possible to have a movable comb hive without the expense of frames. The latest type of catenary hive is approximately equal to the outer dimensions of the Langstroth Hive (505 mm × 405 mm × 240 mm) and is very simple to construct.

Costs of Hives

Basically the cost of a hive is directly proportional to the volume of timber used and the labour/machine tool costs. Both steadily increase with inflation. The cost of timber is considerably less if bought in quantity, and beekeepers' organisations would help their new members considerably by making bulk purchases of timber machined to size. Organised beekeepers can construct hives themselves

for as little as £3 to £6 (1976) without much bloodshed and with little perspiration.

Construction of Modified National, British Deep, Langstroth and Smith Hives

Construction of these hives is similar except for the different dimensions of rectangular components given in the table.

The British Deep is identical to the Modified National except that the brood box is 312 mm (12.3 in.) deep and the frames are 305 mm (12 in.) deep compared with the Modified National brood box of 225 mm (8.9 in.) deep with frames 216 mm (8.5 in.) deep. The British Deep is recommended by the author in preference to the Modified National for the following reasons:

- it is cheaper, because no brood extension is required as is often the case with the Modified National
- the brood box holds very adequate stores for wintering, thus eliminating the necessity for supplementary feeding
- the larger area of comb available to the queen promotes quicker build up of the colony in spring
- the larger combs reduce the danger of isolation starvation.

The Ministry of Agriculture, Fisheries and Food Advisory Leaflet 367, *The British National Hive*, gives full details for home construction. Advisory Leaflet 445, *The Smith Hive,* gives full details of this less complicated hive. These are obtainable from Ministry of Agriculture, Fisheries & Food (Publications), Tolcarne Drive, Pinner, Middlesex, HA5 2DT.

The Catenary Hive

The Catenary hive with honey super. It is thought that entrances near the top of the curve at the front of the hive give greater security and shelter for the bees. The entrance is a $1\frac{5}{8}$ in. diameter hole

The Catenary hive body (brood box) and an example nylon reinforced wax foundation on which the bees build comb to the shape of the hive body. The foundation is supported by two strips of wood which rest on the support which also locates the curve

When bees produce wax and build honeycomb, they hang in festoons from the bar which is to support the comb. These festoons or chains of bees, when freely suspended, form a curve. The natural shape of the honeycomb built when free from restrictions such as rectangular frames and square hives, conforms to the mathematical catenary. This shape gives maximum strength for minimum use of material. Bees do not live in a square world like man. They are not geared to the saw bench and the right angle. At honey shows, men set themselves up as judges of honeycomb and knock off points for holes in corners of combs in rectangular frames. Bees are kept in little houses with sloping roofs and given entrances and even doorsteps on or as near to the ground as possible (W.B.C. Hive). Very pretty, and in fact the general concept of a beehive. An entrance at the bottom of a hive makes it easy for every small creature on four legs to take an interest and possibly gain access to the precious stores within the hive. The bees have to defend those stores to survive. The beekeeper makes life very difficult for bees (a) by giving entrances too near to the ground and (b) by giving entrances which are far too large for circumstances at particular times, especially during periods of minimum activity.

An idea for a queen excluder—slots incorporated in top bar (1975 Askham Bryan College of Agriculture and Horticulture). It is not necessary to purchase metal queen excluders

Frameless reinforced wax midrib ready for use again for comb building. Honey was extracted twice during the summer from these 'combs' and then they were scraped to the midrib after being filled at the heather.

Nylon reinforced wax foundation held in position by two 11 mm × 11 mm bars as used in the brood or hive body of the frameless catenary hive. The bees will build comb on this foundation and extend it into a natural catenary shape
The nylon net gives strength at the weakest point of the comb

The Catenary Hive gives facilities to the bees to build natural combs without the expense and labour caused by using frames, and yet the combs are movable for inspection. The shape of the hive gives the maximum comb area for the bees using a minimum volume of timber and labour. Thus capital expenditure on each hive is greatly reduced when compared with the square hives.

But to operate these frameless hives, it is necessary to use nylon-reinforced wax foundation to give strength to the natural comb. You will have to DIYS. Thus you can actually be completely independent of the equipment vendors. See 'Making your own Foundation' (pages 39–42).

Only one size of nylon-reinforced foundation is used in the super and in the hive body. Although this foundation is rectangular, the bees will extend it to form a naturally shaped comb in the catenary-shaped body of the hive. The nylon reinforcing gives strength at the weakest point of the comb, i.e. where it is attached to the bar and subject to great leverage when handled.

Catenary hive body parts

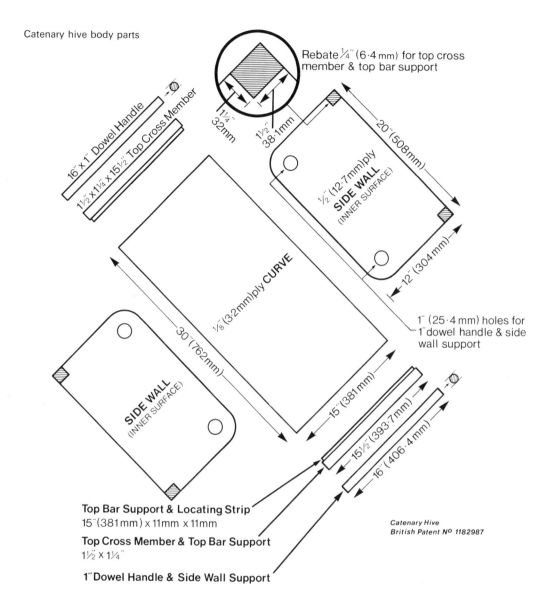

Rebate ¼" (6·4 mm) for top cross member & top bar support

16" x 1" Dowel Handle

1½ x 1¼ x 15½ Top Cross Member

1¼" 32mm

1½" 38·1mm

20" (508mm)

½" (12·7mm)ply
SIDE WALL
(INNER SURFACE)

12" (304 mm)

⅛ (3·2mm)ply **CURVE**

30" (762mm)

SIDE WALL
(INNER SURFACE)

15" (381 mm)

15½" (393·7mm)

16" (406·4 mm)

1" (25·4 mm) holes for 1" dowel handle & side wall support

Top Bar Support & Locating Strip
15"(381mm) x 11mm x 11mm

Top Cross Member & Top Bar Support
1½ x 1¼"

1" Dowel Handle & Side Wall Support

Catenary Hive
British Patent No 1182987

Construction

Hive Body: the two side walls of 12.7 mm (½ in.) exterior ply 508 mm × 304 mm (20 in. × 12 in.) are held in position by two cross members 394 mm × 38 mm × 32 mm (15½ in. × 1½ in. × 1¼ in.) at the top, rebated into the two side walls, screwed and glued. Two dowels 406 mm × 25.4 mm (16 in. × 1 in.) provide a handle and support approximately 50.8 mm (2 in.) from the bottom corners of the side walls.

The curve is 762 mm × 381 mm (30 in. × 15 in.) of 3.2 mm ($\frac{1}{8}$ in.) ply cut across the grain to facilitate bending. Two locating pieces 11 mm × 11 mm ($\frac{2}{5}$ in. × $\frac{2}{5}$ in.) fixed to the top cross members locate the curve and support the bars for the combs.

Honey Super: the honey super consists of two side walls 508 mm × 146 mm × 12.7 mm (20 in. × 5$\frac{3}{4}$ in. × $\frac{1}{2}$ in.) ply nailed or screwed and glued to two end walls of 483 mm × 146 mm × 12.7 mm (19 in. × 5$\frac{3}{4}$ in. × $\frac{1}{2}$ in.) ply. Two bar supports 483 mm × 6.4 mm × 12.7 mm (19 in. × $\frac{1}{4}$ in. × $\frac{1}{2}$ in.) are nailed and glued lengthways 6.4 mm ($\frac{1}{2}$ in.) below the top of the super. Wax foundation is supported by two pieces of wood 11 mm × 11 mm ($\frac{2}{5}$ in. × $\frac{2}{5}$ in.) cut to length for body or super and using metal ends and/or pins.

Queen Excluder: a queen excluder may be a piece of plastic cut to leave 12.7 mm ($\frac{1}{2}$ in.) space round the inside perimeter of the hive body for the bees to gain access to the super when the colony is strong enough and requires space to store honey. This type of queen excluder was used successfully many years by the late Miss Margaret Logan, Adviser in Beekeeping, North of Scotland.

Roof: the roof of the hive is again made from 12.7 mm ($\frac{1}{2}$ in.) exterior grade ply deep enough to accommodate 102 mm (4 in.) thickness of insulation (polystyrene or polyurethane foam) which should be protected to prevent the bees from chewing it. 1.5 mm ($\frac{1}{16}$ in.) ply or vinyl wallpaper may be used. Inside, the roof and the interior walls of the hive should be painted with a flat black paint or dag to minimise condensation.

Siting the Hive

To establish a colony of bees in a catenary hive use a prime swarm or all bees from a colony about to swarm (an artificial swarm). Site the new hive with the top bars and foundation running magnetic North to South. If your entrance hole (41 mm [1$\frac{5}{8}$ in.] diameter) is on the curve, then the entrance will be facing SSE to South. Bees build comb under the influence of gravity and magnetic forces, so it is a good idea to set up the hive properly to obtain the best comb building possible under the prevailing conditions.

The frameless combs of honey can be extracted by uncapping and centrifuging in the normal way. Although the combs might tend to collapse when spun radially, the honey comes out and the comb can be straightened and used again and again thanks to the nylon reinforced midrib. A framed acrylic sheet crown-board is a very worthwhile luxury 508 mm × 406 mm (20 in. × 16 in.).

Wax

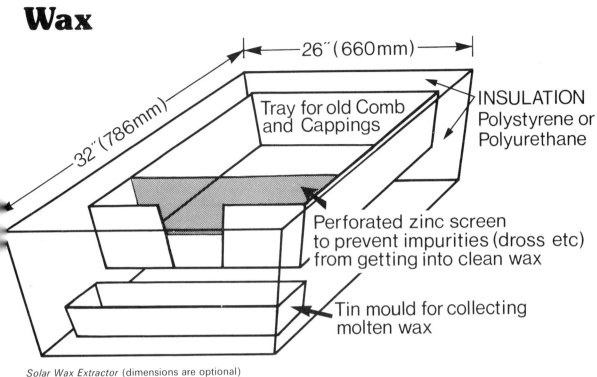

|← —— 26″ (660 mm) —— →|

32″ (786 mm)

Tray for old Comb
and Cappings

INSULATION
Polystyrene or
Polyurethane

Perforated zinc screen
to prevent impurities (dross etc)
from getting into clean wax

Tin mould for collecting
molten wax

Solar Wax Extractor (dimensions are optional) consists of a tin tray with a perforated zinc (or other metal) screen with an opening to allow molten wax to run into a mould. The whole is set up in an insulated box with a double glazed lid. Beeswax melts at about 63°C (145°F)

Solar Wax Extractor

This is a simple device which every apiarist should possess. It consists of a tin tray in an insulated box covered by one or two thicknesses of glass. The lower end of the tray has an opening and is shaped in such a manner that the molten wax will pour out into another mould or tin from which you will take your block of beautiful wax the morning after the day the sun shone—and you will be surprised how often the sun shines even in little old England. Above the opening in the large tray, a piece of perforated zinc is fixed to catch the inevitable lumps of debris—pollen, cocoons and wreckage—which you do not want in your posh block of wax. Make a large solar extractor and be satisfied to melt a little wax at a time and often.

There are steam wax extractors and a fiendish device called an 'MG (Mountain Grey) Wax Extractor' noted for its ability to cover any kitchen ceiling with wax if not operated with care and understanding. Actually it is an excellent piece of equipment and here is how to use it:

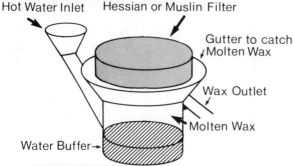

Hot Water Inlet   Hessian or Muslin Filter

Gutter to catch Molten Wax

Wax Outlet

Molten Wax

Water Buffer→

MG wax extractor

1. Measure the capacity of the extractor in pints or litres. Make a note.
2. Pour 1.1 litre (2 pints) of hot water into the extractor which is placed on a stove. This water acts as a cushion between the wax and the source of heat.
3. Add wax (as clean as possible) until you have molten wax to within 38 mm (1½ in.) of the top of the extractor. Do not overheat. Wax does not boil; it vapourises and is highly inflammable, so remember the melting point is about 63°C (145°F), and **do not** allow it to exceed 100°C (212°F).
4. Brief your assistant. You will shortly require a continuous supply of hot water (71°–77°C [160°–170°F]) to pour down the spout to raise the level of the wax in the extractor to about 38–40 mm (1½–1⅗ in.) from the hessian (or muslin) filter. The exact quantity to be measured in pints or litre (you having measured and noted the capacity of the extractor).
5. Lay newspaper all over the floor. Lock all doors. Place your mould or tin (which should be large enough to hold 4.5–5.4 kg [10–12 lb.] of wax) under the outlet of the catchment gutter.
6. Clamp the filter in position.
7. Start to pour hot water and continue to pour until the exact quantity calculated has been used. The water level in the extractor will rise, forcing the wax through the filter. It will run into the gutter and into your mould. **Do not stop the flow** or the wax will set quickly and then the pressure will build up and puncture the wax. Heigh-ho, that is when molten wax will hit the ceiling and you will be in trouble. You should stop pouring hot water just before the water level causes water to come through the filter.

To prevent the block of wax sticking to the mould, simply moisten the inner surfaces of the mould with a detergent liquid. To release the block of wax from the mould, immerse the whole mould in cold water. The wax should float to the surface.

Making Your Own Foundation

Wax foundation for beehives is expensive and can be a regular and costly item in a beekeeper's budget. From the day you extract your first harvest of honey you will have a supply of beeswax. The more honey your bees produce, the more wax you will get. The best wax is that obtained from cappings and it has to be free of sticky honey, so wash it. First soak the wax in clean rainwater (or distilled water) or tap water providing it is **not** hard water. If you live on a limestone belt your water supply will not be suitable unless it has been treated. Honey absorbs water and if left overnight, the mixture of honey, wax and water can be filtered through muslin to separate the wax and leave a dilute honeywater solution that can be used as a must for making mead.

It is important that the wax is clean and free of honey. The clean wax can then be spread out on a double thickness of newspaper in a sunny corner to dry before the next stage of production.

Notes:
- the surplus wax is remelted
- to aid removal of wax from the working surface it is advisable to spray with detergent solution
- **Volume of trough,** e.g. 36 cm long × 20 cm wide × 2 cm deep = 1,440 cm³ = 1.5 litre (approx. 2¾ pts).
- quantities: 2⅔ pts of water + 2⅔ pts of Kaffa Dee
- never give wax foundation to bees unless they can use it. Bees can only build honey comb when there is a honey flow on or during warm weather when they are being fed with sugar syrup.

Making Your Own Foundation

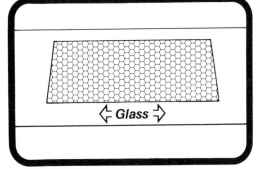

(1). Shows a piece of commercial foundation glued to a piece of glass of good size. Use a contact adhesive. The sheet of foundation needs to be 13 mm (½ in.) longer and 13 mm wider than the sheets of foundation which are to be made. The foundation should be cut to suit the inner super dimensions, leaving a bee space, 6 mm (¼ in.) next to the hive and below

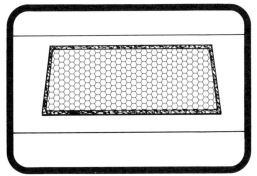

(2). A 6.4 mm (¼ in.) border of vinyl floor tile is glued around the edge to provide a shallow trough for surplus wax—bottom mould

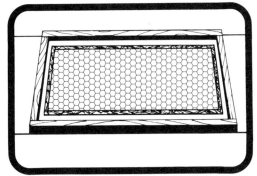

(3). A framework of 25 mm (1 in.) sq. pieces of wood is glued to the glass approximately 13 mm (½ in.) from the edges of the foundation. The trough so formed must be watertight. Strips of Sellotape can be taped to the inside faces of the framework pieces and the tape run on to the glass to aid a good seal. Plasticine can be used at the corners

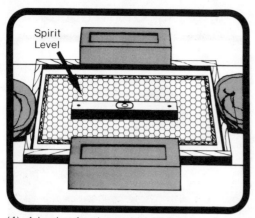

(4). A level surface is essential. Weights can be used to provide a better seal but they may not be needed

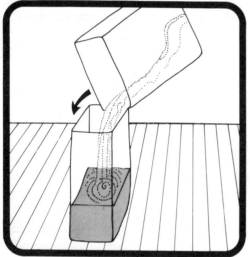

(5). A mixture of equal parts by volume of Kaffa Dee Dental Plaster and water is thoroughly mixed. The volume of water used equals the volume of the trough (see end)

(6). The mixture is carefully poured into the trough avoiding splashing. Speed is not essential. The mixture has the consistency of thin custard

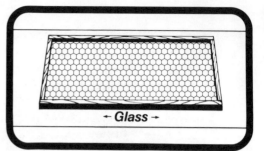

(7). A mould for the top mould is prepared similar to the bottom one, only in this case the wood is placed right up to the foundation edges. The foundation is the same size as the bottom one

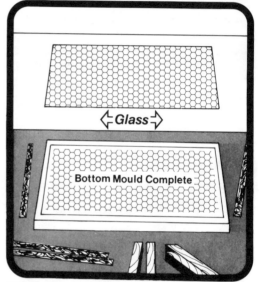

(8). After approximately two hours the mould is carefully removed

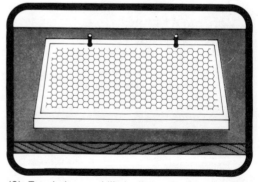

(9). Two holes are drilled adjacent to the edge of the *pattern* on the bottom mould. The holes can be continued into a suitable board for a working surface. Two pegs are pushed through and these serve to align the top mould and hold the bottom mould in position on the working surface. Your moulds are now ready for use

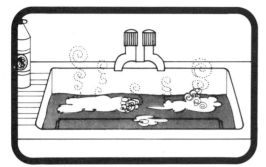

(10). The moulds are soaked in hot water to which a tablespoonful of washing up liquid has been added

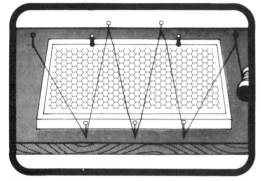

(11). Slots are cut using a thin hacksaw blade in the raised edge of the bottom mould to take wires which can be stretched from nails in the working surface. If nylon reinforced foundation is required, nylon net (similar to the net used for bee veils) can be cut to size and stretched over the bottom mould immediately before pouring the wax. In this case slots are not necessary

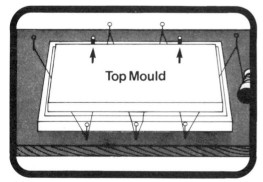

(12). The top mould is placed in position and the cells will arrange correctly automatically. For guidance, marks are made on the back of the top mould corresponding to the raised pegs

(13). A mixture of 44 parts by weight of wax and 1 part by weight of microcrystalline hardener is prepared and melted to 100°C (212°F). This is poured on to the level bottom mould

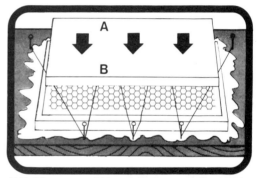

(14). The top mould is quickly but carefully placed on top, leading edge (A) first, and (B) lowered to prevent air locks. Again the cells align correctly. The wax is allowed to set

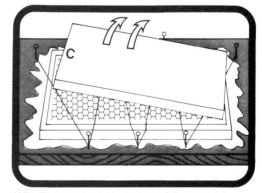

(15). The top mould is then carefully removed, raising end (C) first

(16). The wax is cut around the outer edge of the bottom mould and the sheet is lifted clear

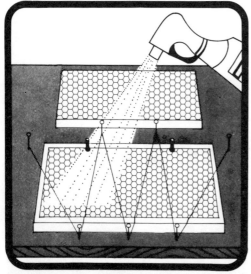

(17). The moulds are sprayed with the same hot detergent solution as they were soaked in ready for making another piece. Use an atomiser. This is important for mould release

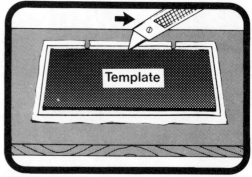

(18). The foundation is cut to size using a template

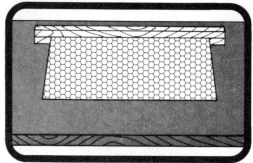

(19). The foundation can then be mounted in a suitable frame—wooden or wire. Nylon-reinforced foundation may be used without a frame if accurate bee-spacing around the foundation is provided. Usually the dimensions of such foundation are equal to the outer dimensions of a frame

Thanks are due to Alex Palmer and John Seed of Normanton Grammar School, West Yorkshire, for their work on the plastic mould method of foundation making.

Bees in Winter

Food consumption by individual bees at different temperatures

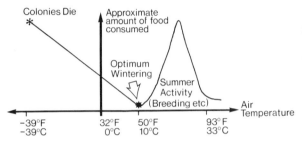

Optimum Wintering

The graph gives an idea of the amount of food consumed by individual bees at different temperatures (still air). Dr J. B. Free and Dr F. Simpson of Rothamsted Experimental Station found a correlation between the respiratory metabolism of the honeybee and the amount of food consumed by measuring one of the products of respiration, i.e. carbon dioxide at different temperatures.[*] This work was of vital importance to beekeepers as it led to the realisation that for optimum wintering, as far as minimum food consumption is concerned, 10°C (50°F) is the best temperature. As long as a colony of bees is not actually breeding, the bees can be said to be comatose, a condition not unlike that of the queen bumble bee or queen wasp during winter. These insects rely entirely on the food stored as fat bodies in their own bodies for sustenance. Thus in winter, when the honeybee colony is not breeding and with air temperatures around 10°C, food consumption is practically nil.

Heat Loss

Generally, queen honeybees stop laying in September and start to lay eggs again often during the first warm spell in January. During this period, especially if mild conditions prevail (around 10°C), food consumption is at its lowest. As the air temperature falls below 10°C some of the bees take food (honey stores) and become more active, releasing energy as heat to maintain living conditions. The higher the rate of heat loss from the hive, the more food will have to be consumed to generate heat to replace heat lost.

The rate of heat loss increases as the difference between the optimum temperature (10°C) and the outside air temperature gets greater—i.e. at very low temperatures bees must consume a lot of food to maintain the heat to sustain life. Free and Simpson found that the lowest temperature at which a colony could no longer stay alive was minus 39°C (minus 39°F). There is a difference in temperature between the

[*] See *The Respiratory Metabolism of the Honeybee at Different Temperatures,* by Free and Simpson.

bees on the outside of the cluster (bees form a cluster within the hive during cold weather) and those on the inside of the cluster; and there is a gradual interchange of position between 'outer' bees and 'inner' ones.

Losses of heat mean losses of honey; thus, good insulation of hives is essential. Through air currents carry away heat and neutralise the benefits of insulation. Just like every other animal, the well-being of bees depends on warmth and comfort, protection from the elements and an adequate supply of food.

Sugar Syrup

Honeybees do not hibernate in winter, nor do they go to sleep. They reduce their activities to a minimum to conserve their stores of food, in order to survive. Colonies of bees that continue to breed into winter rapidly use up their stores and die of starvation. Nature is a hard mistress and the beekeepers who feed lots of sugar to their bees are going against nature and natural selection. This is a rash statement because sometimes it is very necessary to feed sugar syrup—emergencies do arise from time to time due to the weather or mis-management. It happens in the best of circles and when bees are starving they must be fed—not the odd pint of syrup (0.7 kg [1½ lb.] sugar to 0.6 litre [1 pt] water), but a gallon or more.

Mention has already been made of the queen starting to lay eggs possibly during a relatively warm spell in January. The actual time of this event is bound to vary from colony to colony and in some instances it will be well on into February before this critical change

of behaviour takes place. The old books tell us not to interfere with bees in winter and how right they are. If bees have ample stores (11–16 kg [25–35 lb.] of sealed honey) by the end of September and have good accommodation, then you have no need to worry about starvation until the end of March (depending on the severity of the winter). On no account be tempted to peep into a hive during January and February. Don't touch. Don't even clump about near the hives. When you see large pollen loads being taken into a hive, it is perfectly safe to check the food situation, but don't go pulling out combs until it is warm enough to feel comfortable in your shirt-sleeves and breeches. If you observe that when most colonies are taking in large pollen loads, one or two hives are only taking small loads, suspect trouble—possibly queenlessness—and check. If queenlessness is confirmed, unite the colony to a queenright colony forthwith.* A queenless colony in spring is useless, but the bees may be used to boost a small queenright colony.

Condensation in Beehives

When a moisture-laden atmosphere comes into contact with a cold surface, i.e. a surface at a lower temperature than the atmosphere itself, then that atmosphere can no longer hold its water content and droplets of water form on the cold surface. Just breathe on a window.

The products of respiration are carbon dioxide and water, hereafter called CO_2 and H_2O. We have already discussed how a colony of bees has to work harder to convert honey into heat energy to maintain life as the air

* See 'Colonies at Strength', page 18.

temperature falls further and further below 10°C (50°F). The harder an animal works, the greater becomes the respiration rate and the greater is the production of CO_2 and H_2O. Cold beehives cause higher rates of respiration; more H_2O is introduced into the atmosphere within the hive and there will be more condensation, causing poor living conditions. Insulated hives reduce the rate of loss of heat, food consumption, respiration, the amount of H_2O produced by the bees, the amount of condensation and, finally, the need for ventilation—the main culprit as far as loss of heat is concerned. Ideally, an internal surface of black dag paint (as used on internal combustion engines) on a highly insulated surface will prevent condensation *in the vicinity* of the winter cluster. This black surface will absorb some of the heat radiated by the bees, and as the heat cannot escape, that surface temperature will be a fraction of a degree above the temperature of the air in contact with it. Result: no condensation.

For most economical wintering, hives should be highly insulated and *completely* draughtproof.

Isolation Starvation

Colonies of bees can die of starvation when there are adequate supplies of food in the hive which are not accessible under prevailing conditions of temperature and comb arrangement. The normal hives available on the market have entrances situated centrally and at the bottom of the hive. This arrangement derives from the early movable comb hives when man gave the bees a little house with a sloping roof and a door with a porch and doorstep (160–200 years ago). It is the natural behaviour of bees to station the cluster between the entrance and the stores of food for protection. All manner of insects and animals would rob the bees if they did not do this! Thus at the beginning of winter, the bees are centrally clustered and generally in the area between the entrance and winter food supply.

Cold Ways

If the combs are *cold ways*, i.e. at right angles to the entrance extending from front to back of the hive, then as stores are consumed, the cluster will tend to move from the centre to the right or left of the entrance consuming stores towards one side of the hive and getting isolated from the other side where the food remains untouched. If continuous cold weather prevails and the bees run short of stores, they will not be able to move back across the hive without being frozen or chilled and the result will be isolation starvation.

Warm Ways

If the combs are *warm ways*, i.e. parallel to the entrance extending from side to side of the hive, then as the bees consume stores they move backwards away from the entrance, but nearly always remain in contact with food, thus considerably reducing the possibility of isolation starvation.

Definitely have combs warm ways for winter. In summer, manipulations are easier with combs warm ways. But in very hot weather—cold ways *might* be better for the colony, but more important is the fact that new combs should be built in the direction of magnetic north to south.

Moving Bees

If you are determined to produce as much honey as possible from a limited number of colonies of bees, then you will have to be mobile, i.e. you and your apiary. In Australia, the apiarists move their bees at regular intervals distances of over a thousand miles. They follow the honey! We have talked about the various major sources of honey and you will find it profitable to move your bees to these sources.

Do's and Don'ts

It would be a good idea to list a few 'do's', 'don'ts' and 'nevers'! Do have a policy of *never* carrying beehives. They are heavy (or should be) and even though you equip yourself with one of the dozens of patent hive carriers, it is time-consuming and unproductive. Do a minimum of lifting. Remember each time you put a hive down it should be level and preferably kept clear of damp ground by means of hive stands, stones or bricks. There is a difference between lifting a hive to the ground and carrying it. Do try to obtain a trailer, properly sprung and damped so that the bees get a smooth ride. Why not a mobile platform to hold 20 hives or so? You could then leave the hives on the trailer, and move from crop to crop, cutting out the lifting or, should we say, most of it. Unfortunately, trailers and mobile platforms need maintenance, so once a year you are faced with unloading the hives to spring clean them and the trailer. But bees winter well in hives on platforms some 0.6 m (2 ft.) above the cold damp earth.

Never move bees during a honey flow unless there is an emergency such as a spray warning. Thousands of colonies of bees are killed or suffer losses each year as a result of crop spraying. If your bees are on a trailer, you can easily move them. But during a honey flow moving bees is risky. Hives are likely to be almost full of fresh honey, and to close entrances when bees are fanning and ripening honey could be disastrous. The bees could panic in their efforts to get out and continue the ventilation necessary for the processing of honey. Overheating could cause the wax honeycomb to collapse under the weight of honey and a colony of bees can drown in its produce.

Do try to travel at night if you are moving to a crop. Close the entrances as soon as the last bees return. Travelling screens should have been fitted during the day so that roofs can be removed for adequate ventilation as soon as the entrances have been closed. Always use travelling screens. You can put a wet cloth in one corner to provide a water supply if it is a journey of more than one hour. Don't move bees until two or three days after the end of a

Early Catenary hives on trailer at Fountains Abbey

honey flow. They will travel much better.

In terms of short distances, a hive of bees should not be moved more than about 1 m or 3 ft.; thus you can only move a hive across the garden by a series of daily short moves, and then only during flying weather. For the same reason, that is that the flying bees will always return to their located home, a hive of bees must not be moved less than 3 miles! At this distance or more, the flying bees will reorientate to their new location and fly normally.

Remember to do all you can to minimise stress when moving bees, as stress can cause the spread of some bee diseases.

Nectar Sources

What is Nectar?

Nectar is an aqueous, sugar-containing secretion of plant glands called 'nectaries'.*

Nectaries occur on various parts of plants which are above ground. Nectaries serve to regulate the sap pressure within plants and may be described as 'sugar valves'.

Good growing conditions as a result of fine weather causes plants to secrete nectar in various quantities and qualities.

The nectars from different plants contain different values of sugars and minerals, but there is a considerable water content which varies from plant to plant and with temperature and humidity at any given time.

When Does Nectar Become Honey?

Nectar *starts* to become honey immediately it enters the bees' honey sac (stomach). Enzymes (secreted from glands in the head and thorax of the bee) mix with the nectar as it passes from the mouth parts into the honey sac. The three main enzymes (diastase, invertase and glucose oxidase) invert and convert nectar into honey, but not immediately. Incoming nectar becomes part of a complex organisation of food exchange between bees. There is in fact a food chain. The more often the food is passed from bee to bee, the richer the enzyme content of the honey.

Before the honey is sealed, it goes through a ripening process. The water content is reduced by evaporation, a process which can take up to three or four days.

During a major honey flow, a colony of bees can evaporate over a gallon of water during one night's work. A visit to an apiary early on a summer morning or late evening during a honey flow is a fascinating experience. The hives have become busy factories. Honey is being processed. Warm moisture-laden air is being pumped out by numbers of bees, heads down, tails up, wings revving continuously. This stream of vapour meets the cold outside air and gives up some of its water content to form a rivulet on the alighting board or ground in front of the hive entrance. Inside the factory, bees are secreting wax and using it to build honeycomb; others are transporting and exchanging honey, controlling temperatures and humidity within fine limits, tending the queen, feeding brood, sealing brood and honey cells, storing pollen, using pollen, secreting brood food (bee milk), feeding drones and also performing a number of unknown activities. But all this large-scale activity of the colony is due to the presence of a major source of nectar within a short distance

*See *Honey, A Comprehensive Survey*, by Eva Crane, Bee Research Association.

of the apiary and, of course, fine weather.

Major UK Sources of Nectar

Spring: dandelion, fruit blossom, sycamore, other Acer species, hawthorn (not often) brassicas, raspberries

Summer: field beans (sometimes), brassicas, clover, wild mint (*Mentha aquatica*), lime (fickle yielder!)

Late Summer: ling (*Calluna vulgaris*), willowherb (*Epilobium augustifolium*), balsam (*Impatiens glandulifera*).

Minor Sources

If your bees are within range of gardens or public parks, trial gardens or arboretums these will provide valuable minor sources of honey throughout the year, i.e. weather permitting. You can call this your 'background honey flow'. It provides a stimulus to breeding and helps maintain the food supply. Beekeepers can help themselves to increase this background supply of food by cultivating specific plants and being generous to folks in the neighbouring streets. Just a few of these plants are suggested:

anchusa, arabis, asparagus, aubretia, alyssum saxifrage, berberis, borage, buddleia, broad bean, broom, canterbury bells, campanulas, clarkia, candytuft, cornflower, crocus, clovers, collinsia, echinops, fruit trees, gilia, godetia, heather, hyssop, hollyhocks (single), lavender, limnanthes, lime, lupin, marjoram, michaelmas daisy, mignonette, malope, nasturtium, nepeta (cat-mint), *phacelia tanacetifolia,* rosemary, runner beans, sage, snowberry, cotoneaster, scabious, snowdrop, sunflower, sweet alyssum, thyme, toadflax, veronica, wallflower, willow, winter aconite.

There are publications giving much detail of sources of pollen and nectar obtainable from Bee Research Association, Hill House, Chalfont St. Peter, Gerrards Cross, Buckinghamshire, England, e.g. *Trees and Shrubs Valuable to Bees* by M. F. Mountain and *Plants and Beekeeping* by F. N. Howes (Faber & Faber).

Extracting Honey

Honey should be on the hive or in the pot, so sayeth Harry Tasker. Never take combs of honey from the bees unless you are geared to extract honey straight away and, if possible, before the honey has time to cool. Warm honey flows freely and a temperature of 80°–85°F is ideal for extracting. At lower temperatures the job gets more and more difficult until the honey is so thick it will not budge. Some honeys crystallise rapidly (brassica honeys) in the comb and require special treatment. The commercial men work round the clock to harvest their honey. Their aim is to get the honey as quickly as possible into the storage tank, and the empty combs back on to the hives for refill.

But don't let us talk of the big boys and storage tanks. Maybe you cannot afford even the minimum of extracting equipment at this stage. Before removing the honey from the bees you should have a plan of action: first to get the honey from the hive and secondly to extract it from the combs.

Clearing Bees from Honey *

There are several methods of taking the combs of honey from the hives and the methods used depend largely upon the scale of operations and local conditions.

For the man with one or two hives: the simplest way (not necessarily the best way!) is to drive as many bees as possible down into the hive by gently puffing smoke over the tops of the combs. Firmly and quickly take out each comb, giving it a good shake and brushing off the remaining bees. Place the combs in an empty box or super and keep covered (to prevent robbing). The honey should be taken into the house immediately or the bees will have it back (and you too, possibly). Note that no extra equipment is necessary for this method and as you develop skill you will become quicker at the job, which is better for both bees and keeper.

For the hobbyist beekeeper: a crown board (clearer board) fitted with two unidirectional traffic (bee traffic of course) devices known as Porter Bee Escapes is a valuable piece of equipment. The idea is to lift the super of honey off the hive on to the clearer board and then lift both back on to the hive. Thus you separate the bees in the honey super from the queen and the main body of bees in the brood nest. More important is the fact that these bees will have no chance of obtaining enough of that all-important queen substance unless they go down through either of the two escapes, which they will do within 24 hours. Perhaps the odd bee or half dozen bees will not manage it, but 24 hours later you can carry your super full of honey into the house. Do

* See Bee Research Association Reprint, *Clearing Bees from Honey Supers.*

remember that your hive should have no gaps or holes which could allow bees to get into the honey super during the period it is above the clearer board, for given half a chance, the bees will recover the honey which you have stolen for your own pleasure and delight. (Their very survival depends on their store of honey.) This method is almost clinical, but has one major drawback: it entails two visits to the apiary, one to put on the boards and a second journey to remove the honey supers. Incidentally, two Porter Bee Escapes are more reliable than only one, as occasionally an odd drone may block the route.

An excellent method for getting bees into sections for section honey production is to remove the honey super on to a clearer board as for clearing bees; but before putting these back onto the hive, place the box of sections directly on to the top of the brood nest (without any queen excluder) and then place the clearer board and honey super on top. The bees will go down into the sections en route to the queen, and if there is a honey flow, you will get beautiful section honey. And really, you cannot call yourself a beekeeper unless you can produce sections of honey. The production of section honey gives the greatest pleasure and satisfaction, and the removal of boxes of completed sections is probably the pinnacle of apicultural achievement. Go to it.

For the sideliner: use a repellant, Benzaldehyde, to drive the bees down out of the honey super. *Warning:* This chemical is *dangerous*. It is highly volatile and *precautions* must be taken when using it. Otherwise there is a chance that it will not only drive the bees out of the honey super, but completely out of the hive; and in addition it will put you and your assistant into hospital. However, it is certain that the discriminating and thoughtful use of Benzaldehyde has made beekeeping easier. Firstly, the fumes (in moderation) repel bees and secondly they cause a degree of subjugation which is desirable during all manipulations. A method of applying Benzaldehyde is to cut three squares of old flannel sheet 500 mm (20 in.) square. Soak in water. Squeeze out the cloths and spread out on top of each other. Sprinkle the equivalent of one teaspoonful of Benzaldehyde as evenly as possible over the top cloth. Fold all three cloths together and squeeze to spread the chemical. Place them in a tin or plastic bag (to prevent vaporisation) until used.

To drive bees out of honey, just be satisfied to do one super at a time on each hive. Place one of the impregnated cloths directly on top of the honey combs. Allow about 1–3 minutes before taking out each comb of honey and placing it in a bee-tight empty box. You will quickly develop the simple technique of knocking or brushing the few remaining bees off the bottoms of the combs. Always remember that you must get the bee-free combs of honey into the house or they will have it back, and that is for certain.

Actually Getting the Honey
You have brought the honey into your warm room (27°–30°C [80°–85°F]), and now for a bit of sticky business. To maintain good relations with other members of the household, spread newspapers all over the floor. A wash basin with hot water must be available. You must don a clean overall. The

surroundings must be perfectly clean and hygienic because after all, you are handling food, and food should be absolutely clean. (See 'Judging Honey', pages 63–5.)

For the man without any equipment but plenty of enthusiasm: borrow the largest pudding mixing bowl or some hygienic vessel (yes, even one of those would do!). Obtain some muslin and make a square frame to support the material (why not take the seat out of a dining-room chair?). You are simply going to take a tablespoon and scrape the honeycomb down to the mid-rib, scraping the wax and honey into the muslin through which it will filter into the bowl—providing the air temperature in the vicinity is 80°–85°F. This is how people obtained honey for thousands of years, except that they tended to put the brood as well as the honey into the muslin. Nowadays we manage to keep the brood separate from the honey thanks to the use of queen excluders. The honey will be clean and pure enough to bottle immediately. Do not delay, honey is hydroscopic, i.e. it absorbs water and will deteriorate until safely sealed in a jar.

The contents of the muslin will now be sticky wax. This can be scraped into an empty container with a view to washing the wax with soft water. The water is then used for making mead and the wax for making foundation or candles, etc.

For the man with a honey extractor: well there are honey extractors of varying sizes from 2-frame hand-driven to the mighty 2000-frame room-sized extractors used by the large commercials in South America.

The principle is that of the centrifuge. The honey combs are uncapped and rotated in such a manner that the honey is flung out on to the wall of the extractor to run down and collect in the bottom of the machine which has a tap for running off the honey. There are two basic types of extractor; in one the combs are whizzed round tangentially, and in the other, radially. Some extractors like the Taylor's Whirlwind are capable of both tangential and radial extraction. Unless you can get a second-hand bargain, you are likely to pay upwards of £60.00 (1976) for a machine which will last for generations, so it really is a good investment to purchase a new extractor.

Uncapping the honey can be done without any expenditure, but only for a limited quantity of say up to 90 kg (200 lb.) of honey. Above this amount you will be considering more efficient means of uncapping, such as an electrically heated uncapping knife. Again, as your production level rises you will need an electrically heated uncapping tray. This is a most useful device consisting of a sloping metal tray heated by water. Cappings fall into the tray, melt and run through a coarse filter into a vessel. The wax floats to the top of the warm honey in the vessel, and when cool, you have a cake of wax on top of all the honey which fell with the cappings on to the tray. Just one cautionary word about the quality of the honey thus obtained. Heating destroys the enzymes in honey and produces a substance known as hydroxymethal-furfuraldyhyde which, although harmless, is not present in natural honey. So you should not sell this honey for table use as it may not conform to the standards specified by the Codex Alimentarus of the European Community. Nevertheless, there is a good market for cooking honey.

Assuming you are going to uncap with the household carving knife, a good cappings container can be adapted from an old type of rectangular enamel bread bin. Strap a wooden strip across the top to support the frame whilst you uncap. If you examine a comb of sealed honey you will observe an air space between the honey in the cells and the wax cappings. Your first aim is to move the knife through this air space separating the cappings from the honey before spinning. Your second aim is to take a full sheet of cappings off at one stroke of the knife! This is frightfully difficult, but one can counsel perfection and get better results.

When the combs have been extracted, they will be wet with honey. Some keepers like to store combs 'wet' for two reasons. Firstly, when wet stored combs are given in honey supers the bees take readily to the supers and need no better encouragement to store honey. Secondly, wet combs are not so readily attacked by wax moth larvae during storage.

Other keepers like to give the supers of wet combs to colonies in late summer as a preliminary to winter feeding. Thus the bees gain vital food supplies, and the keeper can store his combs all clean and tidy. You pays your money and takes your choice.

And then there is the little matter of that old bread bin full of honey and cappings. Well, after the Sunday roast, the cooker will still be hot, so why not just pop it in for two or three hours. The wax will melt, the honey will drain and when cool you will be able to pour out the honey from beneath the wax cake and use this honey for cooking. The wax cake can be soaked in soft water and the honey water could possibly be used for mead making. When free from honey, the wax should be flung into the solar wax extractor for the sun to complete the job of giving you a fair piece of wax for use as you wish.

Finally, if you become ambitious, electric uncapping machines can be obtained. A typical set-up is to have one of these machines between two eight-frame extractors. One man can extract six tons a day if properly equipped.

Extracting Honey Crystallised in Combs

A phenomenon of recent years has been the increased acreage of oilseed rape grown as a break crop in various parts of the world. Rape is a major source of honey, and given fine weather large crops of honey are being obtained. Unless extracted immediately it is capped, rape honey may crystallise in the comb and you will have to cope. The method recommended is to scrape the honey combs down to the mid rib on to a heated uncapping tray. As soon as the crystals have melted, the honey runs off and can be recovered, but be wary of possible damage to the honey through heating.

Heather Honey

A familiar sight in August on moors such as the Whitby Pickering moors, are rows of hives brought to get a honey crop from the flowering heather. Unfortunately, these hives are some-

Heather honey press

cannot be extracted as easily as 'flower honey' or 'tree honey'. It presents a problem to beginners as it appears that yet another piece of expensive equipment is needed, i.e. a heather press. Heather honey is 'thixotropic'. If the honey gel is agitated, it becomes liquid for a time and is extractable with the normal centrifuge extractor. To agitate the gel, devices called 'honey looseners' are used. These consist of large numbers of needle-like plungers mounted so that they can penetrate the honey in the comb sufficiently to liquefy it prior to extraction.

Alternatively, the honey comb can be scraped to the midrib into a muslin or hessian bag and allowed to drain as previously described. Again, a temperature of 80°–85°F is necessary.

Heather presses can be purchased and these work on the principle of scraping to the midrib (or by placing the whole comb into muslin) and pouring the mix into a hessian or muslin bag which is squeezed under great pressure to force the honey through the bag which retains the wax and acts as a filter. No further filtering is necessary and the honey can be bottled immediately.

times placed in straight lines and too close together. Bees cannot count and disease could spread like a moorland fire.

Heather honey (i.e. honey from ling [*Calluna vulgaris*], which is not really heather) is not a liquid. It is a gel. It

Ailments of Honeybees

All plants and animals are subject to viruses, bacteria, parasites and genetical troubles. The honeybee is no exception. One important and interesting fact is that honeybee ailments are *not* transmittable to mankind.

However, certain types of disease can be disastrous if not controlled. There are laws which have been introduced for the benefit and protection of honey producers in different countries. In the UK the Ministry of Agriculture, Fisheries and Food is responsible for the administration and enforcement of the *Foul Brood Diseases of Bees Order 1967*. Under this order, the appointed officer has powers to inspect your bees and prohibit movement of bees within a given area should a case or cases of Foul Brood be verified.

It is terribly important that you know what to do if you suspect that your bees have either American Foul Brood or European Foul Brood. You should immediately report your suspicions to either your local association secretary or your area Foul Brood Officer. If you do not know either, report to the nearest Ministry of Agriculture, Fisheries and Food office. Do give every assistance and every ounce of encouragement to the chap who has this difficult job to do. Give as much information as possible so that he can check every colony in the vicinity of your apiary. Get your local association to organise a lecture on bee diseases every year so that you can become familiar with the symptoms, even though you may never actually see any of the diseases.

American Foul Brood

Cause   Virus: Bacillus larvae.

Symptoms   Moist, dark-coloured sunken cappings, some perforated. The larval remains eventually dry out to form scales. Foul smell.

Test   A matchstick dipped into the larval remains when removed draws out a brown, ropy thread of the semi-fluid contents of the cell.

European Foul Brood

Cause   *Streptococcus pluton.*

Symptoms   Death of 4 to 5-day old larvae. Dead larvae become discoloured, turn brown and decompose. Foul smell. Often the disease is accompanied by *B. alvei* and/or *Streptococcus faecalis.*

Both diseases are spread by the transference of millions of spores from colony to colony. The spores may be present in honey and certainly in the alimentary canals of infected bees.

Drifting bees and robbing bees may spread the Foul Brood Diseases and good spacing between hives is essential to reduce the spread of the disease.

Acarine

Cause   Parasitic mite *Acarapis woodi.* The mite breeds in the trachea of the honeybee entering through the first thoracic spiracle.

Symptoms   Crawling bees, bees trying to fly; dead bees.

Test   Remove head and expose trachea. Staining or discolouration of trachea (may be seen through a pocket magnifier) will indicate infestation.

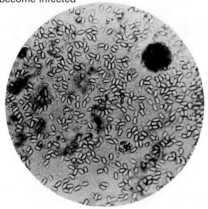

Treatment Apply acaricide, e.g. Folbex, at intervals to kill off the adult mites before breeding. A strip of Folbex is allowed to smoulder within the hive and a series of treatments should suppress the infestation.

The disease is spread by adult mites migrating from infested bees to young bees. These mites have the ability to enter the honeybees' trachea if the bee is less than nine days old. The main cause of the spread of the disease from hive to hive is again robbing and drifting bees.

Nosema

Cause *Nosema apis,* a spore-forming micro-organism which develops and multiplies in the gut of the honeybee.

Symptoms Spring dwindling of the colony. Dysentery stains around the entrance to the hive. Staining within the hive.

Test Crush 30 abdomens of bees using pestle and mortar. Dilute with drop of water. Smear on slide (400 to 600 magnifications) will reveal thousands of spores.

Treatment Apply Fumidil B in sugar syrup as directed by the manufacturers. This is an antibiotic. Destroy all old combs and get the colony on to new ones.

The disease is spread by the ingestion of spores through the mouth parts. The spores become active on reaching the mid-gut of the bees and multiply. Millions of spores are voided in the excreta of infected bees. Infected colonies are prone to dysentery and may foul the interior of the hive, especially during winter. Other bees clean up and become infected. The combs themselves become infected and may be a source of infection. The incidence of Nosema can be reduced by constantly disposing of old comb and encouraging bees to build and live on new comb.

The main factor in the spread of Nosema is *stress* which may be caused by the transportation of bees, bad and untimely manipulations of colonies, too frequent inspections, poor local conditions, bad hive conditions.

Paralysis

Causes Paralysis viruses, poisons.

Symptoms Bees unable to fly; crawling bees; shiny black bees.

Test Viruses cannot be seen except with electronic microscopes, so it is necessary to submit samples to a laboratory for confirmation of the disease.

Treatment Some strains of bee have an inherited immunity to virus paralysis, and the only known cure is to replace the queen of an infected colony.

There are several minor diseases of bees and the reader is recommended to read *Infectious Diseases of the Honeybee* by Leslie Bailey, M.A., Ph.D., of Rothamsted Experimental Station for a complete account of this negative side to Honey Production.

Feeding Bees*

There is an increasing tendency these days to make this as easy as possible. There are advocates for feeding candy instead of sugar syrup. This is accentuated by the fact that commercial sugar candy fondants are fairly easy to come by and are fairly easy to give to the bees. Warnings about this have been given before but I think they should be emphasised. First of all it should be made clear that any form of candy which is given to bees for storage purposes gives the bees work which they would not otherwise have to do. Bees are in the habit of collecting nectar which is a dilute solution of sugar. They continue this habit when they are given candy upon which to feed, and they immediately dilute this candy from their own body water content until they succeed in reducing the sugar content of the candy from about 82 per cent (at least) to something around 40 per cent. They then evaporate the surplus water until they have a sugar solution which approximates to 80 per cent and then they store it. This is useless work. The faultiness of this method of feeding is accentuated if it is realised that these same bees have to fly from the hive in search of water in order to make good their body water losses. It would have been easier to have given them a concentrated liquid sugar solution in the first place which they could have stored with far less effort and with no necessity for the bees to leave the hive in search of water. A similar criticism can be applied to the feeding of dry sugar. Water has to be collected to replace that which has been lost in converting the sugar into a sugar solution of 40 per cent. Work is then demanded of the bees to concentrate this to a solution of approximately 80 per cent before it can be stored. Furthermore, any grains of sugar which are too large for the bees to handle are thrown out of the hive entrance and are wasted. Feeding dry sugar is therefore a trebly wasteful method of autumn feeding, although it may well be a very satisfactory method of maintaining a starving colony during spring and summer and is also useful in establishing a swarm on new combs. It is all really a matter of applying common sense and of not being too easily misled by what one reads or hears.

There is another point of importance. Invert sugar candies such as one can buy commercially are produced by the acid-hydrolysis of sucrose (everyday sugar as we buy it in the shops). Some of them are made using the mineral acid, hydrochloric acid. Others are produced with the help of the organic acid, tartaric acid. As far as bees are concerned there seems to be no dis-

57

* An article by Alfred Hebden, NDB.

tinction between the two. Both are equally harmful to bee life if they are fed to them *in the absence of any other form of food and for a continuous period*. Invert sugar candies shorten bee life by about two-thirds and produce dysentery in the process when they are fed alone, and this seems to apply to all makes irrespective as to whether mineral or organic acid was used in the manufacture. It seems wiser, therefore, only to use these candies in an emergency and not as a staple diet. If a colony of bees is starving to death, candy may well keep them alive. If the bees have to rely upon such candy for much more than a week they are likely to be in trouble. The best food for bees is nectar produced by flowers which the bees are equipped to handle at all times. They can consume it or store it at their pleasure. Failing this, they should be fed sucrose, which is every-day sugar, obtainable from the corner shop. During spring and summer this can be given to them as 40 per cent solution (1 lb. of sugar in 1 pt. of water) and in autumn as an 80 per cent solution (2 lb. of sugar in 1 pt. of water). This is the advice given in every textbook upon beekeeping, and is still sound counsel. The bees can handle these solutions to suit their needs with the minimum of work and with no risk at all. To stress this point a little further, I can only add that solutions of the darkest kinds of unrefined sugars such as molasses, treacle and golden syrup are lethal to bees and they cannot survive for long if they are fed on them alone. And, although I cannot see anybody doing it, bees will be damaged if they are fed on their own honey if it has been over-heated and then fed back to them. We hear a great deal of talk these days about human beings being better for living on natural unadulterated foods. Bees are just the same. Every since I have kept them I have been convinced that they ought to be allowed to live on honey all the time and that they should be fed sugar only in an emergency or when they could not gather sufficient honey for their survival. I have never had any sympathy at all with the view that bees could be robbed of honey which they needed (because it could be sold at so much per pound) and that this could be replaced with sugar (at much less per pound). It looks as though this view-point is now being substantiated after investigation into the value of feeding various sugar compounds and that our ancestral beekeepers have been right all the time. To be fair, though, it could have been the other way.

Alfred Hebden was County Bee-keeping Adviser for the West Riding County Council for many years in the 1940s and 50s. During World War II, Winston Churchill was instrumental in allowing the keepers of bees a special sugar ration to keep the bees alive. The numbers of beekeepers increased during this period when lawns and parks were transformed into allotments to help the nation grow more food. Alf Hebden was very conscious of the possible harmful effects of feeding various sugar concoctions to bees and kindly gave his permission for his article to be used in this book.

Stings

Before becoming too involved or committed to keeping bees, you should have been to a few apiaries and have got an idea of what protective clothing is desirable. You should also have been well and truly stung. If you happen to be the one person in a million to react adversely, i.e. become unconscious and finish up in hospital, then clearly you would be well advised to confine your honey producing activities to the extracting, bottling and packing department. Otherwise, just encourage others to do the beekeeping and buy honey from them.

A few people react badly but not seriously enough to give up the idea, and many beekeepers have found that they develop a degree of immunity to the sting. The human physiology does to some extent create antibodies to bee venom, and the initial pain and swelling soon disappears. However, stings on some parts of the body, especially parts of the face, can be a little distressing for a short time. A good sting up the fingernail can cause excrutiating pain and the best of us apiarists will have watery eyes if stung on the nose. Most of us have retreated at some time or other feeling somewhat demoralised. However, there are antidotes and there is a procedure to minimise the effects of a sting.

- remove the sting as soon as possible by pushing it out of the skin with the fingernail (and remember that little old sting can penetrate again and the sting pump will still be working although the bee has torn itself away to die)
- spray the area with Wasp-Eze, a proprietary aerosol, taking care to protect the eyes
- forget all about it or enjoy it.

Adrenalin ointments can be effective. Someone will tell you to rub with vinegar or methylated spirits or use the blue bag. Well everyone feels better if something is done but that is the psychological therapy!

If a person reacts abnormally when stung, i.e. shallow breathing and loss of control, get them to a doctor or hospital within 20 minutes.

Making Pure Beeswax Candles

Pure beeswax candles produced from wax made by the Fountains Abbey bees

There is a kinship between man and bees, and this can be felt most strongly when one becomes involved in making candles from beeswax. For millions of years, it is possible that man got light, warmth and comfort from beeswax candles. The fragrance of a burning beeswax candle gives a room an aura which is indescribably beautiful. The textures and scents of different beeswaxes can give enormous pleasure. Each harvest of honey brings its harvest of wax and each wax is slightly different in colour. Beeswax candles show off each other. Two quite ordinary moulded candles can suddenly look superb when placed alongside a slightly larger candle of a different colour. Never add dyes to pure beeswax; the natural colours of wax are most satisfying.

Candlemaking is a craft, a marriage of art and science. There are three principal methods used: moulding, dipping and casting. Whilst the most perfect candles must have the cleanest and lightest coloured wax, it is possible to make excellent candles from dirty, discoloured wax. So do not fuss about the quality of your wax unless you are going to exhibit, when of course, the judges will take wax quality into account.

Moulding

Moulds can be obtained from candlemakers' suppliers. Plain glass moulds of various sizes may be used and the technique is slightly different from that used for the rubber and plastic moulds. Moulds can be made but you would be well advised to limit any aspirations in this direction until you have gained an understanding of the raw material and its behaviour at different temperatures.

Dipping

A large rectangular shaped vessel (in a water bath) capable of holding 9–14 kg (20–30 lb.) of molten wax is necessary. About 24 wicks weighted and suspended from a board are dipped at regular intervals into the molten wax. Some 15 to 20 dips should ensure a satisfactory thickness of wax sets around the wick. The diameter of the candle should be appropriate to the gauge of the wick used. This applies to all candles.

Casting

This consists of pouring wax from a ladle down a wick, twisting the wick whilst pouring. This is a method used for making tapered candles.

Beeswax melts at about 63°C (145°F). It is recommended that wax be protected from overheating (which will tend to darken it) by using a water jacket—i.e. always put the wax pot into a pan of water to raise the temperature for pouring wax into moulds at about 82°C (180°F). You must use a thermometer when handling wax or honey. It is no use guessing or things will go wrong.

Moulds should be thoroughly clean and prepared carefully before pouring. You must use the correct size of wick. The candle wick must be properly made. You cannot use any old bit of string, and it is best to purchase several different gauges of wick right at the start of your candlemaking. Construct a shallow tray about 230 mm (9 in.) square by 25 mm (1 in.) deep. Drill holes in the bottom for the different sized wicks. Thread short lengths of each wick through the holes and fill the tray to a depth of 13–19 mm ($\frac{1}{2}$–$\frac{3}{4}$ in.) of beeswax with your various candlewicks protruding from the top of the wax. You have now constructed a wick testing bed! By the way, before using candlewick, it must be thoroughly impregnated with wax. To achieve this submerge the lengths of wick in very hot wax for a few minutes until the hot wax is no longer frothing or bubbling—this is the moisture being driven out of the wick material. Having made your wick test bed, you can carry out burning trials! Allow each wick to burn for fifteen to twenty minutes. It will melt an area of wax according to the gauge of wick. The diameter of the molten wax in the test bed should be equal to the diameter of a candle most suitable for that particular gauge of wick. If a wick is too small for a candle, it will burn a deep cavity and become nothing more than a night light. If a wick is too large it will not be able to get enough fuel and it will smoke when burning.

Having decided which wick to use and having cut it to length and impregnated it with wax, you must prepare the mould by rinsing it with a solution of detergent which is to act as a mould release. A solution of one teaspoonful of stergene in a cupful of warm water should be poured into the mould and moved around to wet the interior surface without producing soapy bubbles. The mould should then be inverted to drain, the aim being to leave a moist film of detergent on the inner surface of the mould.

Meanwhile your wax is melting and approaching 82°C. Check often. When the mould is thoroughly drained of surplus liquid using a wicking needle the wick should be threaded through the tip of the mould, and if necessary sealed with mould seal. Generally the wax cools quickly enough to self seal. Make sure the wick is straight and centrally situated and the mould supported firmly. If you have no proper mould supports, suitably sized glass jars may be used. Even a round hole cut in a cardboard box will suffice. Just to be on the safe side, it is a good idea to fix a muslin filter over your wax can so that any foreign bodies are prevented from getting into your mould when you pour in the hot wax at 82°C.

Try to pour down the wick. Having poured the wax, put the can back into the water bath to retain its temperature, because as soon as the wax starts to set around the edge of the mould you will need to 'top-up'. Cooling wax contracts, and to prevent a hole from forming in the bottom of the candle you must 'top up' at just the right moment! That's it. There is nothing more you can do until the following day when the wax will be completely cold and set. To remove the candle from its mould it helps to immerse the whole mould in cold water. The candle should float out of a glass mould quite easily, but the plastic and rubber moulds must be very carefully peeled off using soap on the outer skin to prevent friction. Be careful not to dig your fingernails into the wax.

Polish gently with damp towelling. Gradually the candle comes to life. The damp towelling prevents scratching which can occur as a result of dry polishing causing local hot spots. The final polishing must be done with a soft cloth. Remember that dust is an abrasive so keep your candles clean by polishing lightly but often. Trim the wick to 13 mm ($\frac{1}{2}$ in.), cutting diagonally.

The Judging of Honey

A fundamental requirement is that the honey and its container should be clean. Entries containing debris or crystals may be rejected without further examination or tasting. Small particles of wax and hairs up to 2 in. are typical faults which can eliminate exhibits before the actual judging of the honey starts. Many excellent honeys will be rejected because of poor presentation. It is also true to say that medium quality honies will often be amongst the awards if well presented.

Clear Honey

Clear honey is usually divided by colour into three classes: light, medium and dark. Colour grading glasses may be obtained from the British Bee Journal, 46 Queen Street, Geddington, Nr Kettering, Northants.

Appearance: generally, a good honey has a bright and attractive appearance and catches the judge's eye immediately, but appearance can be vetoed by density or flavour.

Aroma: a good aroma may be detected when the lid is first removed from the jar. No aroma could indicate that the natural volatile oils in the honey have been evaporated by heating during preparation. Marks should be awarded for aroma.

Density: density (weight per unit volume) is important and should be at least 1.415 at 60°F (15°C). Low density honeys are liable to ferment because of high water content. Density and viscosity (rate of flow) are both subject to temperature variations. Where honey is staged just prior to judging, there may be large differences in temperature between exhibits, e.g. Mrs X may have kept her honey in the fridge to obtain greatest density and viscosity, whilst Mrs Y may have kept her honey in a warm cupboard next to the fire to prevent crystallisation. However, it is not often one has to resort to the use of thermometers and hydrometers to assess density. Usually the denser honey has a slower rate of flow, and many judges merely tilt the jar or observe the rate at which the depression fills after taking a sample of the honey for tasting.

Flavour: flavour is closely associated with aroma. Honey from major crops such as clover, field beans, sycamore and lime usually has a recognisable taste, but a judge is liable to encounter honey which may be described as exotic. Such honey will have a certain attractive aroma and delicate flavour, as for example, honey from the wild mint *(mentha aquatica)* which grows in profusion in some damp areas. Marks for flavour should be awarded carefully, avoiding if possible personal preference but paying regard to what, in your opinion, would be the taste of the experts and public in general—a difficult decision to make as one often encounters two excellently flavoured honeys with quite different flavours!

2. Crystallised Honey

Four out of every five bottles of honey consumed in the UK are crystallised. As usual, the exhibit must be clean and it is good practice to invert the jar and examine for debris and dust which may have settled on the base.

Aroma: crystallised honey is liable to ferment, and on removing the lid of the exhibit any alcoholic smell will denote the presence of fermenting or fermented honey. Such an exhibit must be completely rejected. The aroma should be pleasant, although much less pronounced than in clear honey exhibits.

Texture: a fine smooth grain is desirable. The honey should be firm but not hard. The top of the honey should be free from liquid.

Flavour: the sample should be taken from the top corner of the jar, as any fermented honey will most readily be detected here. The honey should be smooth and have a delicate · and delightful flavour. Coarse and gritty honey should be faulted.

Frosting: crystallised honey is often spoilt by a contraction of the honey from the side of the jar, giving a frosted appearance. This may happen to the best honey in the show, and frosting should be regarded as a minor fault.

3. Comb Honey

When judging comb honey, it is often more satisfactory to deduct marks for faults.

Cleanliness: the wax cappings and frame should be perfectly clean.

Weight: combs suitable for extracting or pressing should be heavy. Credit must be given for weight.

Straightness: wavy comb surfaces with cappings forming concavities which would make uncapping tedious are factors for deduction of marks.

Freedom from Pollen: cells containing pollen may be detected by examining the comb in front of a bright light (powerful torch is recommended), and the presence of pollen may be regarded as a fault.

Wax Cappings: the wax cappings should be dry and even over the whole surface. Weeping cells may be regarded as a fault. There should be no uncapped cells. Uncapped cells, especially containing honey, should be regarded as a serious fault.

The Honey: careful examination for crystallised honey in the cells will reveal whether the honey is extractable. Crystallisation indicates ageing and is a serious fault.

Aroma: the comb should have a fresh and attractive aroma. It should not smell foisty or mouldy, this being an indication of age.

4. Beeswax

Usually a minimum weight has been stipulated on the schedule. The wax should be clean and free from embodied debris and discolouration. Excessive heating in the preparation of wax for exhibition causes a darkening of colour, and the better exhibits will be light in colour.

Aroma: wax has a distinctive and pleasant aroma which should be easily detected. Marks should be deducted for negligible aroma.

Texture: when beeswax is broken, the crystalline texture will be visible. The larger the crystalline formation, the better the wax. Usually it is sufficient to break away a small portion of the edge of the wax without spoiling the exhibit.

Equipment Recommended

■ honey grading glasses
■ spatulas (several)
■ tissues (for drying spatulas after cleaning)
■ *honey hydrometer ('Densitaster' obtainable from *British Bee Journal*)
■ *thermometer
■ torch (for detection of impurities)

*Not essential

Final Note: when beset with the problem of awarding a prize to one or the other of two exhibits which are equal in merit but different in flavour, a fastidious examination of the lid and honey jar may reveal a slight flaw or inferiority. But it is more encouraging to make a joint award if this is possible.

Reference: Beekeeping Techniques by A. C. S. Deans (Oliver & Boyd).

Cooking with Honey

(From a lecture at Askham Bryan College of Agriculture given by Mrs R. E. Clarke, NDB.)

Honey can be introduced into cooking in many ways. It combines well with fruits (fresh or dried)—see 'Honey Punch', 'Honey Grapefruit' and 'Strawberry Dish', also 'Apricot Conserve'.

It can be used well with spiced—see Plum Chutney, etc., and in rich cakes where it will help keep them moist, or plain cakes where it will give flavour in addition to sweetening.

As a glaze for meats—see bacon recipe, and add to this roast lamb glazed with honey and chopped mint.

All cooks will enjoy experimenting with honey and many recipe books are available, from American and Australian sources in particular.

Honey Fruit Punch

The hot weather energiser

Fruit juices as available *can* include pineapple, orange, grape, grapefruit. *Should* include with above, some lemon juice. To 3–4 cups of fruit juice add 2 cups of water and 4 tablespoons of honey. Dissolve honey in warm water and add to blended juices. Chill thoroughly and serve cold.

Dried Apricot Conserve

$1\frac{1}{2}$ cups dried apricots well washed, dried and minced

$\frac{3}{4}$ cup blanched sweet almonds chopped finely

2 cups honey heated in double boiler to 200°F

METHOD

Stir all together and store in small sterilised jars well sealed. This makes an excellent lunch pack filling.

Honey Raisins

$\frac{2}{3}$ cup flour sifted together with $\frac{1}{2}$ teaspoon baking powder and pinch salt

$\frac{1}{2}$ cup honey

2 small eggs

$\frac{1}{2}$ cup chopped nuts

$\frac{1}{2}$ cup chopped raisins

METHOD

Beat eggs and add honey gradually. Stir in fruit and nuts, and sieve in dry ingredients and stir lightly. Spread in a well greased pan and bake in a moderate oven for about 35 minutes. Allow to cool a little and cut into squares or bars.

Honey Glazed Bacon

Parboil any selected bacon joint or bake until partly cooked in a slow oven (a little cyser in the cooking is pleasant). Remove rind, score fat in patterns and decorate with cloves if liked. Take one cup of pineapple and stir in one cup of honey. Spread this over the ham and return it to the oven to finish cooking, basting several times.

Honey Cereal Rings

5 cups rice crispies or corn flakes

1 cup toasted coconut or $\frac{1}{3}$ cup chopped nuts

$\frac{1}{2}$ cup honey

$\frac{1}{4}$ cup sugar

Small tablespoon butter

METHOD

Heat honey with sugar in double boiler to 246°F. Add butter and cereal with nuts if used and stir well. Mould in ring and use filled with fruit, ice cream or jelly. (The recipe can be made into balls and used as sweets.)

Honey Chocolate Cookies

$\frac{1}{2}$ cup shortening
$\frac{1}{2}$ cup honey
1 small egg
$\frac{1}{2}$ cup chocolate chips
Chopped nuts various as liked
1 cup flour double sifted
1 teaspoon baking powder
Pinch salt
Egg spoon of vanilla essence

METHOD

Beat honey and shortening until white and fluffy in texture. Beat in egg. Add vanilla essence followed by sifted flour, baking powder and salt, and fold in nuts and chocolate chips. Allow to cool and drop in teaspoons on to baking sheet well greased or covered with oiled paper. Baking takes about 12 minutes at 365°F or regulo 5.

Honey Fluffy Frosting

1 egg white
Pinch salt
Small half cup of slightly warmed honey

METHOD

Beat egg white with salt to stand in peaks. Run honey in a fine stream into egg white, beating constantly as honey is added. (Takes just over 2 minutes with electric beater.)

Ripe Tomato Chutney

12 lb. tomatoes
1 lb. onions (if liked)
$\frac{1}{2}$ lb. granulated sugar
1 lb. honey
$\frac{1}{4}$ oz. paprika
Pinch cayenne
$1\frac{1}{2}$ oz. salt
1 pint distilled spiced vinegar

METHOD

Skin the tomatoes and cut them up. Grate, chop or mince the onions and cook with the tomatoes until thick pulp is obtained. Add half the vinegar and the spices and simmer until thick, then add the sugar and honey dissolved in the remaining vinegar and cook until of a thick consistency. Bottle while hot. Distilled spiced vinegar gives the best coloured chutney, but if not available use ordinary vinegar and add $\frac{1}{4}$ teaspoon mixed spice.

Apricot Jam (Dried Fruit)

2 lb. dried apricots
5 pt. water
3 lb. honey and 3 lb. sugar
6 oz. almonds
Juice of 2 lemons

METHOD

Wash the apricots and soak them in the water for at least 24 hours. After soaking, put the apricots and water in a preserving pan and simmer for $\frac{1}{2}$ hour. Add the lemon juice, sugar, honey and blanched almonds; stir until the sugar has dissolved. Boil rapidly until setting point is reached.

Orange Marmalade

3 lb. Seville oranges
$4\frac{1}{2}$–6 pt. water
1 teaspoon citric or tartaric acid or juice of two lemons
4 lb. honey
2 lb. sugar

All honey may be used but a better set is obtained if some sugar is added.

METHOD

Scrub and scald the fruit, remove the skins and some of the pith from these if very thick, and cut the rind into shreds. Put the shredded peel, any acid and half the water in a pan, bring to the boil then simmer gently for about 2 hours, or until the peel is tender. Cut up the rest of the fruit, pith coarsely and simmer with the remaining water in a closed pan for $1\frac{1}{2}$ hours, and either strain it through a colander to remove the pips and coarse tissue, or rub the pulp through a fine sieve. If preferred, the peel and pulp can be left soaking overnight in basins before cooking. Add the strained pulp to the peel, bring to the boil and boil off excess water if necessary. Add the sugar and honey and stir until this is dissolved, then boil rapidly until setting point is reached. Remove the scum, allow the marmalade to cool slightly and pour into warmed jars. Cover with waxed circules while still hot and tie down cold.

Plum Chutney

2 lb. plums (after stoning)
1 lb. onions grated
8 oz. honey
1 lb. peeled cored apples
1 lb. raisins
1 teaspoon each ground ginger and all spice
$\frac{1}{4}$ teaspoon each ground cloves, mustard,
    nutmeg, cayenne pepper
1 pt. vinegar

METHOD

Cook apples to a pulp with *very* little water, and do likewise with plums; cook onions until soft in covered pan: mix three pulps when cooked. Add spices and half vinegar. Cook until thick. Dissolve honey in vinegar and add to pan. Cook until thick.

MEAD

Mead is made from honey and water, fermented together with fruit acid, tannin, yeast and yeast extract. Spices, etc., are sometimes added, but the result, however good, is not mead.

Honey: For dry mead use a light honey, for sweet dark mead use a dark honey. This is purely based on the colour of sherry and one is prepared for the taste by the shade of the drink. It is often recommended that the mixture of honey and water be boiled to start with. Whilst this will kill any wild yeasts in the must, the essential oils which give the bouquet are driven off. Honey may be sterilised by holding it at 110°F for five to six days in a thermostatically controlled heating box. After that, boiling water is added.

Basic Recipe—Dry Mead

$3\frac{1}{2}$ lb. honey made up to 1 gallon with boiled
    water
$\frac{1}{2}$ teaspoon of citric acid
$\frac{1}{8}$ teaspoon grape tannin
1 yeast nutrient tablet

METHOD

Make up a starter of mead yeast three or four days before you intend to make the mead. Delay making until the starter is working well. Pour sufficient boiling water on to the honey to dissolve it. Dissolve the acid, nutrient and tannin in a little cool boiled water and add this to the must. Pour all this into a sterilised gallon jar and top up with cool boiled water.

When cool enough (70°F) add the yeast starter and fix a fermentation lock. Leave in a warm place until fermentation stops. This may be four or five weeks. Slow fermentation will go on very much longer. As soon as there is an appreciable deposit on the bottom of the jar rack, put into a clean jar. On no account leave the must on the deposit too long. Store in a cool place for at least two years, racking from time to time as necessary. When it is thought all fermentation has ceased, bring into a warmer place, and see if fermentation recommences. If so, leave for a further period and test again. Bottle. Mead goes on throwing a deposit for a very long time, and has a habit of starting to ferment again a long time after one thinks it has finally stabilised.

Sweet Mead

Exactly the same method as above except the original must is made up with $2\frac{1}{2}$ lb. honey with (not in) $\frac{1}{2}$ gallon of water. When the first vigorous fermentation eases, add $\frac{1}{2}$ lb. honey dissolved in as little boiled water as possible. Keep on doing this whenever fermentation slows down, until renewed fermentation follows the addition of honey. Now taste for sweetness, and add more honey until the desired sweetness is attained. For yeast use a sweet wine yeast such as sauterne, malaga, tokay or sherry.

Cyser

(Recipe by Mr S. W. Andrews.)

Cyser is a mead which is made by substituting pure apple juice for water in the mead production. Any apple juice may be used, but the juice of Cox's Orange Pippin and cooking apples to the ratio of 80 per cent Cox's and 20 per cent cookers will produce a very pleasant Cyser.

It is unnecessary to add acid and yeast nutrient to the must. Both of these ingredients are present in adequate quantities in the apple juice, and a little acid will be produced as a by-product of the fermentation.

1 gallon pure apple juice
2 lb. honey (if the juice is from ripe eating
    apples)
3 lb. honey (if the juice is from cooking
    apples)
Yeast (a sedimentary wine yeast such as
    Lachrymal Christie or Tokay is very
    suitable)

METHOD

Mince and press the apples. Put the juice into a gallon jar and add a crushed Campden Tablet, stir and leave for 24 hours. The following day, rack the juice from the pulp sediment. Take 2 pt. of juice and bring to the boil with the honey. Boil for about three minutes and remove from the heat. Skim the froth from the surface, and allow to cool. When the temperature is about 120°F add to the bulk of the liquor. Stir well and add an active yeast culture. Fill a gallon jar $\frac{7}{8}$ full with the must, fit an air lock and place in a warm place. The remainder of the must can be placed in a second container and when the vigorous fermentation is over, the gallon jar can be topped up with new wine from the second container to within 1 in. from the bottom of the cork. Keep the must in a warm place—between 65°F and 70°F is about right. The second part of the fermentation may be a little cooler—60° to 65°F. When the fermentation has ceased, rack the new wine into a clean jar and store in cool place.

Cyser, like all types of mead, will greatly improve with keeping.

Honey Cake

8 oz. Goodwin's extra self-raising flour
3 oz. butter or margarine
2 eggs
$\frac{1}{2}$ gill honey
4 oz. raisins
4 oz. currants
2 oz. citron peel
3 tablespoons milk
Pinch of nutmeg
Pinch of salt

METHOD

Mix together flour, salt and spice, rub in butter or margarine, stir in raisins, currants and finely chopped peel. Next add honey, well beaten eggs and milk. Mix thoroughly. Place in well greased cake tin and bake for $1\frac{1}{2}$ hours in a moderate oven: gas—regulo 5; electricity—400°F.

Honey Fruit Cake

2 cups California dark seedless raisins
1 cup sliced dried apricots
1 cup slivered blanched almonds
1 cup chopped walnuts
1 cup halved candied cherries
2 cups diced candied pineapple
$2\frac{1}{2}$ cups diced mixed candied fruits and peels
$1\frac{1}{4}$ cups shortening
$1\frac{1}{4}$ cups honey
6 eggs
$2\frac{1}{2}$ cups sifted flour
1 teaspoon baking powder
$1\frac{1}{4}$ teaspoons salt
1 teaspoon cinnamon
$\frac{1}{2}$ teaspoon cloves

METHOD

Combine raisins, apricots, nuts, candied fruits and peels. Cream shortening and honey together. Beat in eggs one at a time. Sift flour with baking powder, salt and spices. Blend into batter. Stir in fruits and nuts, mixing well. Turn into greased 10 in. tube pan lined with two thicknesses of greased brown paper and one of waxed paper. Bake in very slow oven, 250°F, with shallow pan of hot water on floor of oven, about 5 hours. Makes one tube cake ($7\frac{1}{2}$ lb.).

Glossary

Bee Yard A term used in North America to describe a number of hives on one site. An apiary.

Brood All stages of development of the honeybee from the egg to the emergence of the adult bee.

Brood Box or Body Where brood rearing takes place. Most beekeepers keep this separate from the honey department by means of a queen excluder.

Brood Rearing New generations of bees are produced from eggs laid by the queen in the compartment of the hive called the brood body.

Colony of Bees Not less than six British Standard Combs covered with bees including laying queen.

Colony Odour A pheromone. This odour is colony specific and enables the bees of one colony to distinguish bees from another colony thus making it difficult for bees to gain access to any hive other than their own.

Drawn Comb An expression to describe honeycomb being built by bees.

Footprint Odour A pheromone. Bees can recognise a place where bees have been before, e.g. a branch used by a swarm or an empty hive, by the odour left by other honeybees.

Foragers Bees which go out and gather nectar or pollen or water.

Honey A sweet liquid produced by bees from nectar (see *Honey* by Eve Crane, published by IBRA).

Honeycomb The home of the honeybee. Built of wax secreted by eight glands in the abdomen of the bee.

Honey Super A place in the hive for the bees to store honey.

Nectar A sugary liquid secreted in the nectaries of plants and especially in the nectaries of flowers.

Out-apiary An apiary at a distance from your home.

Pheromone A complex substance produced by bees which influences the behaviour of other bees of the same species. (Other animals produce their own pheromones.)

Propolis A resinous substance gathered from plants and used by honeybees to seal parts of the hive.

Queen Excluder A device for allowing access to the honey super for worker bees but not the queen or drones.

Skep A beehive made of straw used up to 1850-1950, during which period the movable comb wooden hive became popular. Skeps are now used mainly for taking swarms.

Smoker Device for producing smoke to subdue bees.

Wax Foundation A sheet of beeswax with a honeycomb pattern which provides a base for bees to build honeycomb.

Further Reading

Beginners

Practical Bee Guide, J. G. Digges (Talbot Press O.P.)
The Art of Beekeeping, W. Hamilton (Herald Printing Works)
British Bee Plants, A. F. Harwood (Apis Club Foxton)
Ministry of Agriculture, Fisheries and Food Bulletins:

    No. 100 'Diseases of Bees'
    No. 134 'Honey from Hive to Market'
    No. 144 'Bee Hives'
    No. 306 'Foulbrood'
    No. 328 'Bees for Fruit Pollination'
    No. 330 'Acarine'
    No. 344 'Migratory Beekeeping'
    No. 347 'Beeswax from the Apiary'
    No. 362 'Examination of Bees for Acarine'
    No. 367 'British National Hive'
    No. 412 'Feeding Bees'
    No. 445 'Smith Hive'
    No. 468 'Modified Commercial Hive'
    No. 473 'Nosema and Amoeba'
    No. 549 'Langstroth and Modified Dadant Hives'
    No. 561 'Minor Brood Diseases and Disorders'
    No. 566 'Dysentery in Bees'
    No. 574 'Beekeeping—Making Increase'
Beekeeping in Britain, R. O. B. Manley (Faber & Faber)
Wonders of the Hive, S. A. Lavine (Exeter Press)

Intermediate

Infectious Diseases of the Honey Bee, L. Bailey (Land Books Ltd, B.R.A.)
The World of the Honey Bee, C. G. Butler (Collins)
Honey, Eva Crane (Bee Research Association)
Laboratory Diagnosis of Honey Bee Diseases, H. A. Dade (Bee Research Association)
Anatomy and Dissection of the Honey Bee, H. A. Dade (Bee Research Association)
The Dancing Bees, K. Von. Frisch (Methuen & Co.)
Pollen Loads of the Honey Bee, D. Hodges (Bee Research Association)
Pollination of Fruit Crops, (Horticultural Association, Bee Research Association)
Plants and Beekeeping, F. N. Howes (Faber & Faber)
The Concise British Flora in Colour, W. Keble Martin (Michael Joseph Ltd)
Principles of Practical Beekeeping, Robert Couston
Beekeeping, F. G. Smith (Oxford University Press)
Queen Rearing, L. E. Snelgrove (Bleadon, Somerset)
Swarming, its Control and Prevention, L. E. Snelgrove (Bleadon, Somerset)
A Manual of Beekeeping, E. B. Wedmore (Edward Arnold & Co.)

Advanced

A Dictionary of Biology, (Penguin Books)
An Introduction to Genetics, C. M. M. Begg (English Universities Press)
Intermediate Botany, L. J. F. Brimble (Macmillan & Co. Ltd.)
Beekeeping in Antiquity, H. M. Frazer (Bee Research Association)
History of Beekeeping in Britain, H. M. Frazer (Bee Research Association)
Bumble Bees, Free and Butler (Collins)

The Dance, Language and Orientation of Bees, K. Von. Frisch (Harvard University Press)
The Hive and the Honey Bee, R. A. Grout (Dadant & Sons, Illinois.)
Insect Natural History, A. D. Imms (Collins)
Communication Among Social Bees, M. Lindauer (Oxford University Press)
Honey Farming, R. O. B. Manley (Faber & Faber)
Practical Microscopy, Martin and Johnson (Blackie & Son Ltd)
Agricultural Chemicals Approval Scheme (Ministry of A.F. & F.)
Trees and Shrubs Valuable to Bees, M. F. Moutain (B.R.A.)
Floral Biology, M. S. Percival (Pergamon Press)
The Behaviour and Social Life of Honey Bees, C. R. Ribbands (B.R.A.)
The ABC and XYZ of Bee Culture, A. I. Root (A. I. Root & Co.)
Bees, Wasps, Ants and Allied Insects of the British Isles, E. Step (Frederick Warne)
Preparation of Honey for Market, G. F. Townsend (Ontario Department of Agriculture)
British Plant Life, W. B. Turrill (Collins)
A Dictionary of Science, Uvarov and Chapman (Penguin Books)
The Life of Insects, V. B. Wigglesworth (Weidenfield & Nicolson)
A New School Biology, F. J. Wyeth (G. Bell & Sons Ltd)
Beekeeping Techniques, A. S. C. Deans (Oliver & Boyd)

Acknowledgements

I would particularly like to thank Dr J. B. Free of the Rothamstead Experimental Station for the help obtained from his scientific work made available through the International Bee Research Association. Also for kindly allowing the reproduction of his photographs. I would also like to thank many other friends who have unwittingly contributed to the contents of this little book; especially Alec Palmer and John Seed of Normanton Grammar School.